GIANTS OF ELECTRICITY

GIANTS OF ELECTRICITY

by Percy Dunsheath

ILLUSTRATED

THOMAS Y. CROWELL COMPANY, New York

ACKNOWLEDGMENTS

In the preparation of this book I have drawn on many sources of information, the most important ones of which are collected under Bibliography. Many of these have not been published in English, but with the aid of my wife and two friends, Miss Dora Sowden and Miss Joan Walley, there has been no difficulty in translation from the French, German, and Italian. As far as Latin is concerned, an excellent translation into English from Galvani's original account of his experiments has been published by the Burndy Library, and I acknowledge with gratitude this assistance.

Many friends have helped in other ways. I should like to single out Mr. V. Holmblad of Copenhagen, who supplied local details of the life of Oersted. Other such friends are the librarians of the Royal Institution, Mr. K. D. C. Vernon, and his assistant Mr. M. R. Halliday, who responded generously and with extreme patience to my frequent appeals for help in compiling the chapters on Davy and Faraday in the atmosphere where these two carried out their work. Mr. O. H. Wesencraft of the University of London Library has been a tower of strength in placing his knowledge of the sources of unusual books at my disposal. Finally I must thank the Société des Amis d'Ampère for the sentimental journey which I was able to make to that delightful spot on the slopes of Mont d'Or where Ampère spent his boyhood.

Designed by SALLIE BALDWIN

Manufactured in the United States of America.

L.C. Card AC 67-10471

1 2 3 4 5 6 7 8 9 10

BY THE AUTHOR:

ELECTRICITY: How It Works
GIANTS OF ELECTRICITY

CONTENTS

Dedicated to the memory of those great but humble pioneers in electrical science by whose devotion the secrets of nature have been revealed and applied in the service of mankind, whose achievements have brought men closer together, placed immense power in their hands and illuminated every sphere of human activity.

AUTHOR'S NOTE

As a boy, I had a hobby of constructing electrical devices. Experiment and discovery in this field continued to fascinate me, and later electrical engineering became my profession. As my knowledge increased, so did my admiration for the men who had pioneered in the development of electricity. Admiring them at first for their work and ideas, I later had a chance to learn more about their lives and began to appreciate their personal qualities. They were men who had the same kind of day-by-day family and personal problems that all of us have. They often labored under difficult conditions and suffered professional setbacks. Nevertheless they had enough curiosity, enthusiasm, and strength of purpose to undertake the demanding work of exploring new areas of human knowledge. It seemed to me that the study of the individual characteristics and experiences of these men would be worthwhile, and I decided to write a book about them.

The main problem in making this collection of biographies was in choosing a limited number from the many men whose work was essential to electrical progress. The period covered by the group selected is roughly the late eighteenth and early ninteenth centuries. I have tried to keep a chronological order but there is still considerable overlapping in the lives and work of many of the individuals. Although I did not really attempt to introduce geographical variety, my choice includes representatives from America,

Britain, Denmark, France, and Italy. This accidental distribution of nationalities bears witness to the fact that scientific progress has been a truly international adventure.

Any attempt to write the biographies of men prominent in the development of electrical science within a restricted framework of dates faces the writer with the problem of where to cut into the stream which flows across century frontiers and how to arrange the sequence of events. Birthdays do not occur in a convenient tidy pattern nor indeed do the dates of the important discoveries which make up the story. Previous history of the field covered by the person's activities is a vital factor and his contribution must be appraised according to the state of knowledge at the time. The entire process of discovery is one of building on foundations laid down by predecessors even if on occasion the foundations call for modification to suit the rising edifice.

PERCY DUNSHEATH

GIANTS OF ELECTRICITY

BENJAMIN FRANKLIN

1

BENJAMIN FRANKLIN
1706-1790
and His Forerunners

The foundations of electrical science were laid by experiments and observations made over many centuries. Long ago the Greeks discovered that if they rubbed amber it would attract lightweight particles such as straw. This early contribution to electrical lore is memorialized in the word "electron," which means amber in Greek. William Gilbert of Colchester (1544–1603) borrowed from the Greek language to name the phenomenon he called electric force. The court physician of Queen Elizabeth I of England and president of the College of Physicians, he was awarded a state grant in recognition of his scientific researches. He was interested in magnetism and electricity, and in 1600 he published the first book in England devoted to experimental physics. This book, *De Magnete,* contained a chapter that is the earliest writing ever published on electricity.

One of Gilbert's discoveries, reported in *De Magnete,* was the fact that if a lodestone were broken to separate its two magnetic poles, each new piece would still have two magnetic poles. He recognized that the earth was a great magnet, which, though spherical, had two poles, and he called attention for the first time to magnetic "dip," the tendency of a suspended bar magnet to dip down from a horizontal position so that it pointed to the nearer of the earth's two poles. (Justice was scarcely done for his contribution to navigation by the illustration for the title page in the second edition of *De Magnete*, published in 1628. In the picture, an early mariner's compass, consisting of a lodestone floating in a bowl, is shown adrift on the sea while the ship sails on without it.)

In *De Magnete*, Gilbert distinguished between the magnetic attraction of the lodestone, which passes through other substances, including water, and the electric attraction of amber, "the effluvium of which is choked," as he put it. He examined the electrical properties of many substances and laid the foundation for the later classification of materials as conductors (those which conduct electricity freely) and dielectrics (those which offer resistance to the passage of electricity). Gilbert designed the first electrical instrument, which he called a "versorium" (turnabout), a kind of electroscope used to measure the magnitude of an electrical charge. It took the form of a metal strip which pivoted at the center and rotated when a charged body was brought near to one end.

The next significant advance was the development in 1660 of a frictional machine for generating static electrical charges. Its inventor was Otto von Guericke (1602–1686), the burgomaster, or mayor, of the German town of Magdeburg and a onetime quartermaster of King Gustavus Adolphus of Sweden. Guericke's machine consisted of a sulphur sphere mounted on a wooden axis and rotated by a crank. As the sphere was turned, a dry hand or cloth was pressed to its surface creating friction and causing it to become electrified with a charge powerful enough to produce noisy visible sparks. Using the axis as a handle, Guericke carried the charged sphere about in his laboratory and used it for various experiments. He observed that lightweight objects, such as pieces of paper or feathers, were at first attracted and then repelled by the sphere. Thus, he was the first to notice electrical repulsion between like charges. He also produced the first power transmission line when he passed an electric charge along a length of several feet of linen thread. Guericke's discovery of the possibility of power transmission was later followed up by the English scientist Stephen Gray in his investigations of conduction and insulation. In 1720 Gray published a report explaining how he had conveyed an electric charge over a distance of seven hundred feet using a line of hempen cord suspended by silk threads.

As the scientific interest in electricity developed, more and more attention was paid to increasing the size and power of electric machines. The most remarkable of all the electrostatic machines made in the eighteenth century was the gigantic construction designed by Dr. Martinus van Marum of Holland (1750–1837). Built in 1784, the machine had, as surfaces to generate static electricity, a pair of circular glass plates measuring 65 inches in diameter spaced about 7 inches apart on an axle which could be revolved by cranking. An electric charge was generated on the plates by the friction of pads attached so that they rubbed against the revolving surface of the glass. The charge, which was then transmitted to a system of large brass cylinders, was powerful enough to produce a spark that bridged the space between two of the cylinders when they were set two feet apart. Van Marum's machine, which was used for many experiments to observe "some phenomena on a larger scale," is still preserved at the Teyler Museum in Haarlem, The Netherlands.

Electrical progress took a big step in the mid-eighteenth century when it was found that electrostatic charges could be stored and built up in what became known as the Leyden jar. This apparatus, the earliest form of the electrical condenser, operates on the principle that an electric charge on one body induces an opposite charge on a nearby body and holds it there by attraction. In a condenser, two conductors are brought close together but are prevented from coming in contact by a dielectric. While a charge is built up in one of the conductors (by contact with a charged rod, for example), the other conductor is grounded to allow the opposite charge to escape.

Credit for developing the first jar condenser is generally given to Pieter van Musschenbroek (1692–1761), professor of mathematics and physics at the University of Leyden in Holland. In 1745 he was carrying out experiments with charges produced by a glass globe frictional machine. Hoping to lead the electricity into water contained in a glass jar, he had led a wire from the machine into the jar, which his assistant, Cunaeus, was holding in his right hand. During the experiment, Cunaeus apparently brought his left hand close to the wire to see why no further sparks were coming forward. Since the jar was fully charged, his action short-circuited the electricity from the jar through his body. Musschenbroek then repeated the experiment, taking the place of Cunaeus, and described his experience in a letter written in January 1746 to the French scientist René de Réaumur. "Suddenly I received in my right hand a shock of such vio-

COURTESY BURNDY LIBRARY

The earliest known (1746) illustration of the Leyden jar. The current is generated by the revolving glass globes at the left. When the man holding the jar touches the wire, the circuit is completed and the man receives a very strong shock.

lence that my whole body was shaken as by a lightning stroke . . . the arm and body were affected in a manner more terrible than I can express. In a word, I believed that I was done for."

At the time that Musschenbroek was carrying out his experiments in Leyden, others were similarly interested in the storing of the electric charge. In Germany, E. G. von Kleist, an amateur in electrical matters, was investigating the problem when he received a shock from a nail inserted in a medicine bottle. Although Von Kleist had developed his experiment independently, before the Leyden discovery was reported, Musschenbroek was the first to publish his findings and made a more complete examination of the principle involved. For these reasons he is generally acknowledged as the originator of the Leyden jar, given its name by Abbé Nollet in honor of Musschenbroek's work.

Abbé Antonio Nollet (1700–1770), who assumed the title and dress of an abbé although he was never ordained a priest, was both a showman and a serious student of electrical phenomena. For a time the tutor of the French dauphin, he occupied a high position at the French court and entertained King Louis XV and his retinue by demonstrating the effects of electric shock. On one occasion, he passed a powerful discharge from a Leyden jar through a line of one hundred and eighty guardsmen with hands linked. The effects of shock, felt simultaneously through the line, caused the guardsmen to leap into the air with more than military precision. In another demonstration he assembled seven hundred monks connected to each other by short lengths of wire they held in their hands. At the instant the circuit was complete, the mile-long line of figures jumped into the air as one man, to the great amusement of the king and others who observed the performance.

But Nollet was not just a frivolous dilettante. He taught physics at the Ecole du génie de Mézières and other schools. In Paris he carried out many electrical experiments and published a number of volumes on electricity and other scientific subjects. He was the first to call attention to the fact that pointed objects give out brushes of light when charged electrically, and he made several interesting and fundamental observations on electrical discharge in a vacuum and on the electrical properties of different kinds of glass. He was also the earliest to write about the close relationship between lightning and the electric spark. "Thunder is, in the hands of nature, what electricity is in ours," he wrote in 1748; ". . . those wonders which we dispose at our pleasure are only imitations on a small scale of those grand effects which terrify us." However, when he tested the effects of electricity on animals and plants he reported some results that are not altogether credible. According to his observations, cats and pigeons lost weight when subjected to doses of electricity, while plant growth was increased fourfold.

Across the Atlantic, meanwhile, Benjamin Franklin was acquiring a reputation as a scientist and world authority on electrical theory. Aged forty and already prominent as a publisher and political figure in the North American colonies, Franklin began a remarkable series of electrical experiments in the late 1740's. At the same time, he began a correspondence with leading European electrical experts which continued for twenty years. Much of the material from his letters appeared in the *Transactions* published by the Royal Society of London, which was founded on November 28, 1660, and incorporated by Royal Charter on July 15, 1662, "to improve natural knowledge by experiments." The society awarded him the Copley gold medal in 1753, and elected him a Fellow in 1756.

In his autobiography, Franklin describes his introduction to the study of electricity as follows: "In 1746, being at Boston, I met there with a Dr. Spence, who was lately arrived from Scotland and showed me some electrical experiments. They were imperfectly performed, as he was not very expert; but, being on a subject quite new to me they equally surprised and pleased me."

There is no other historical mention of such a Dr. Spence, but Franklin may have been referring to a Dr. Spencer, who delivered scientific lectures in Philadelphia in 1744. Franklin, living in Philadelphia, would almost certainly have known of these lectures. It is not unlikely that he traveled to

Boston two years later to follow up an interest already aroused. His autobiography continues: "Soon after my return to Philadelphia, our library company received from Mr. P. Collinson, Fellow of the Royal Society of London, a present of a glass tube, with some account of the use of it in making such experiments. I eagerly seized the opportunity of repeating what I had seen at Boston; and, by much practice, acquired great readiness in performing those, also, which we had an account of from England, adding a number of new ones. I say 'much practice,' for my house was continually full, for some time, with people who came to see these new wonders."

The popularity of his performances became an embarrassment to Franklin. After a time he had duplicate pieces of glass apparatus made for carrying on the experiments in frictional electricity and distributed them among his friends. He had an ingenious neighbor, Mr. Kinnersley, who "being out of business, I encouraged to undertake showing the experiments for money and drew up for him two lectures, in which the experiments were ranged in such order, and accompanied with such explanations in such method, as that the foregoing should assist in comprehending the following. . . . His lectures were well attended, and gave great satisfaction; and after some time he went through the colonies, exhibiting them in every capital town and picked up some money."

By way of thanking Mr. Collinson for sending the glass tube, Franklin described his experiments in several letters which Collinson arranged to be read in the Royal Society. The early letters aroused no particular interest within the Society, which did not at first include them in its *Transac-*

tions. However, they were issued as a pamphlet by Edward Cave, the editor of the *Gentleman's Magazine*. Franklin observed the success of this publishing venture with evident satisfaction. "Cave, it seems, judged rightly for his profit," he commented, "for by the additions that arrived afterward, they swelled to a quarto volume, which has had five editions, and cost him nothing for copy money."

In his first letter to Collinson, Franklin modestly expressed the fear that his observations had probably been anticipated by experimenters on the other side of the Atlantic who had been engaged on the subject much longer than he had. He then went on to describe many different electrical phenomena that had come to his attention. He noted that the attraction between a charged body and another object was followed by repulsion after the two bodies had come in contact. He discussed the electric wind caused by the discharge from a metallic point, explaining how it had led him to devise the electric windmill "of which the resulting phenomena, I could if I had time, fill you a sheet." He described how spirits (distilled products) had been ignited by an electrical discharge and how candles, just blown out, had been relighted by drawing an electric spark through their smoke.

One of his inventions in a lighter vein was the electric kiss. According to Franklin's instructions, when a lady and gentleman stand on wax "give one of them the electrised phial in hand; let the other take hold of the wire; there will be a small spark; but when their lips approach, they will be struck and shocked."

Another of Franklin's inventions was his counterfeit spider, "made of a small piece of burnt cork, with legs of linen thread, and a grain or two of lead stuck in him, to give him more weight." To perform the experiment an electrified phial containing a wire was needed. With this at hand, the spider was suspended by a fine silk thread over a table where, wrote Franklin, "we stick a wire upright, as high as the phial and wire, four or five inches from the spider: then we animate him by setting the electrified phial at the same distance on the other side of him; he will immediately fly to the wire of the phial, bend his legs in touching it; then spring off, and fly to the wire on the table; thence again to the wire of the phial, playing with his legs against both in a very entertaining manner appearing perfectly alive to persons unacquainted. He will continue this motion an hour or more in dry weather."

In later experiments reported to Collinson, Franklin studied the Leyden jar. On the basis of his work with it, he challenged the belief of many European scientists that there were two distinct kinds of electrical "fluid"—vitreous and resinous. The scientists had arrived at this view after observing that two kinds of electrostatic charges were produced when such different substances as glass and resin were rubbed. Franklin disagreed with their deduction, maintaining that there was only one kind of electricity appearing on the conductors used inside and outside the Leyden jar in equal quantities and opposite signs, positive and negative. Thus he developed what is known as the "single-fluid" theory of electricity, which he successfully defended against such powerful opponents as Abbé Nollet, with whom he corresponded.

During this stage of his researches, Franklin also discovered that when a hollow metal body was charged, the electricity passed entirely to the outside surface. While working with a plate condenser formed of a sheet of glass between two metal coatings he observed that the charge was stored in the glass. The coatings could be stripped off and replaced by two uncharged sheets which immediately became charged in the same way as those removed.

In 1749 the series of experiments on the Leyden jar and other electrical condensers was brought to a close by a typically Franklin episode. He organized a picnic with some very unusual aspects. His plans for the outing are described in a letter to Mr. Collinson, dated April 29, 1749.

"Chagrined a little that we have been hitherto able to produce nothing in this way of use to mankind; and the hot weather coming on, when electrical experiments are not so agreeable, it is proposed to put an end to them for this season, somewhat humorously, in a party of pleasure, on the banks of the Skuylkil river. Spirits, at the same time, are to be fired [ignited] by a spark sent from side to side through the river, without any further conductor than the water; an experiment which we some time since have performed, to the amazement of many." (For this feat, an insulated spoon carrying the spirit was connected by a wire extending across the river to the outside coating of a Leyden jar on the far side of the river. At the appropriate moment, the knob of the jar was discharged to a rod in the river.) Franklin continues: "A turkey is to be killed for our dinner by the electrical shock, and roasted by the electrical jack, before a fire kindled by the electrified bottle; when the healths of all the famous electricians in *England, Holland, France,* and *Germany* are to be drunk in electrified bumpers, under the discharge of guns from an electrified battery." (The bumper, as Franklin described it, was "a small thin glass tumbler nearly filled with wine and electrified as the bottle was. This, when brought to the lips, gives a shock if the party be close shaved and does not breathe on the liquor.")

Late in 1749 Franklin began his research to establish the relationship between lightning and electricity. Writing to Collinson in May 1750, he discussed at length the "Phaenomena of the Thunder Gusts," including the formation of storm clouds and their mode of electrification. By analyzing observed facts, he was able to offer a fundamental explanation which identified handmade frictional electricity with the lightning discharge of nature. In the letter he also considered the possible use of lightning rods to protect structures but failed to mention the vitally important feature of grounding the rod, without which the device would have been useless and dangerous.

Franklin's ideas on lightning rods and the investigation of thunderclouds were more fully developed when he wrote his next letter to Collinson in July 1750. In part of the letter he described an experiment using a model cloud made of cardboard suspended by silk threads and probably covered with some form of metallic paper so that it could be electrically charged. He observed that the cloud, "when charged, will strike, at near two inches distance, a pretty hard stroke, so as to make one's knuckle ache." In this experiment he was able to draw off the discharge from the cloud by presenting a needle at 12 or more inches distance from it. By varying the conditions of the experiment, he made another important discovery. He found that if the experimenter held the needle when his body was not properly grounded he would feel the electrical shock. When he replaced the needle with a blunt body he observed that the charge from the model cloud was drawn off less efficiently and more violently. "If these things are so," he wrote, "may not the knowledge of this power of points be of use to mankind in preserving houses, churches, ships, etc., from the stroke of lightning, by directing us to fix on the highest part of these edifices, upright rods of iron made sharp as a needle, and gilt to prevent rusting, and from the foot of these rods a wire down the outside of the building into the ground, or down round one of the shrouds of a ship and down her side till it reaches the water? Would not these pointed rods probably draw the electric fire silently out of a cloud before it came nigh enough to strike and thereby secure us from that most sudden and terrible mischief?"

In the same letter, Franklin described the details of a plan "to determine the question whether the clouds that contain lightning are electrified or not." He wrote as follows: "On the top of some high tower or steeple, place a kind of sentry-box, big enough to contain a man and an electrical stand. From the middle of the stand let an iron rod rise and pass, bending out of the door, and then upright twenty or thirty feet, pointed very sharp at the end. If the electrical stand be kept clean and dry, a man standing on it when such clouds are passing low might be electrified and afford sparks, the rod drawing fire to him from a cloud. If any danger to the man should be apprehended (though I think there would be none) let him stand on the floor of his box, and now and then bring near to the rod the loop of a wire that has one end fastened to the leads, he holding it by a wax handle; so the sparks, if the rod be electrified, will strike from the rod to the wire and not affect him."

Franklin's letters on lightning, when read before the Royal Society, were "admired not only for the clear and intelligent stile but also for the novelty of the subject." After

Cave's publication of the letters in 1751 and the appearance of a French translation of them in 1752, many experimenters in Europe set up lightning rods. The grave personal risk taken by these men was dramatized when one such rod brought death to a Professor Richmann of St. Petersburg in Russia. The professor had left his simple electrometer connected to the exposed iron rod while he attended a meeting of the Russian Academy of Science. On hearing a clap of thunder he hurried back to his rod. In his excitement at seeing an appreciable deflection of the electrometer, he came too near his apparatus and was killed instantly by a great flash of white and bluish fire which appeared between it and his head.

One of the Europeans who acted on Franklin's experimental suggestions was a French scientist named D'Alibard, who set up a rod standing 40 feet high at Marly, near Paris. It was by means of D'Alibard's apparatus that the common identity of lightning and electricity was proved for the first time on May 10, 1752. On that day a soldier who was guarding the experiment observed a flash of lightning and charged an electric phial from the sparking rod. When King Louis XV of France received news of this experiment, he commanded that a letter be written to request the Royal Society of London to send thanks and compliments to "Mr. Franklin of Pennsylvania."

Deprived of the opportunity to be first in performing the lightning experiment he had planned, Franklin was very restrained in talking about his famous kite experiment to identify lightning with electricity. In his autobiography he dismissed it with a comment that he would not "swell this narrative with an account of that [D'Alibard's] capital ex-

COURTESY BURNDY LIBRARY

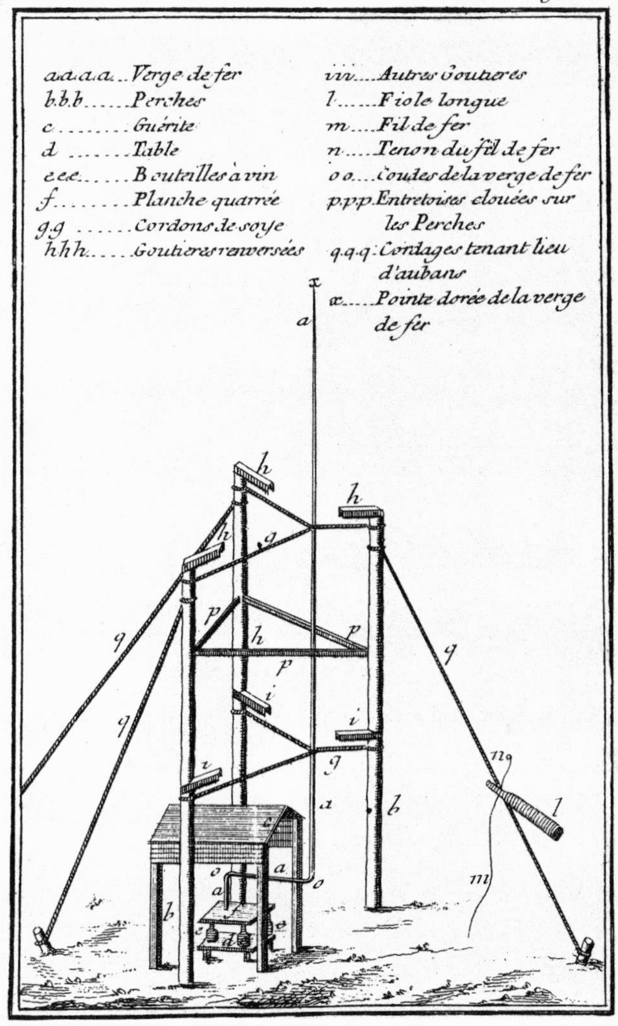

This apparatus was set up in 1752 in France and was used to test Franklin's belief that lightning and electricity were related.

periment . . . nor of the infinite pleasure I received in the success of a similar one I made soon after in Philadelphia . . ." Writing to Collinson in October 1752, he gave instructions for the experiment and suggested the results but did not admit he had tried it. The only person who seems to have gotten the facts about what happened from Franklin himself was Joseph Priestley, who, with Franklin's encouragement, wrote a famous history of electricity published in 1767. In his account Priestley states that "the Doctor . . . was waiting for the erection of a spire in Philadelphia . . . when it occurred to him that by means of a common kite he could have better access to the regions of thunder than by any spire whatever. Preparing, therefore, a large silk handkerchief and two cross-sticks of a proper length on which to extend it, he took the opportunity of the first approaching thunder-storm to take a walk in the fields, in which there was a shed convenient for his purpose." Nothing appeared to happen for a considerable time after the kite was raised. Franklin was beginning to despair of the contrivance when ". . . he observed some loose threads of the hempen string to stand erect and to avoid one another, just as if they had been suspended on a common conductor. Struck with this promising appearance, he immediately presented a knuckle to the key, and . . . the discovery was complete. He perceived a very evident electric spark. Others succeeded, even before the string was wet, so as to put the matter past all dispute, and when the rain had wet the string he collected electric fire very copiously." "This happened," said Priestley, "in June 1752, a month after the electricians in France had verified the same theory, but before he heard of anything they had done."

In the United States Franklin's lightning rod was rapidly adopted to protect buildings. However, his ideas met with more resistance in Europe. In France, one of his opponents was the powerful Abbé Nollet. Two of his supporters there later became famous as leaders of the French Revolution. Maximilien Robespierre, as a lawyer in Arras, once successfully defended the cause of a local landowner who had been ordered to remove a lightning conductor on his house. Jean Paul Marat, who was killed in his bath by Charlotte Corday, was an enthusiastic electrical experimenter whom Franklin saw several times during his visits to France.

In England the matter of lightning conductors was considered by a special committee of the Royal Society. Franklin's evidence in support of sharply pointed rods was accepted by all the members of the committee but one. In the public debate that followed, Franklin's political views may have influenced King George III to throw his support to the blunt-knob advocates. As a result of the controversy, the president of the Royal Society was forced to resign. Nonetheless, in 1769, St. Paul's Cathedral in London was equipped with pointed lightning conductors.

Progress in chemistry during the late eighteenth century helped to improve the understanding of electrical phenomena. Two famous scientists of that time who pioneered in the area of electro-chemistry were Joseph Priestley and Henry Cavendish.

Joseph Priestley (1733–1804) was an English clergyman with very strong opinions, which made him a dissenter in his church and a controversial political figure. He was already interested in science in 1766 when Benjamin Franklin met him in England and encouraged him to write *The History and Present State of Electricity.* The book became famous, and because of it, its author was admitted to the Royal Society of London. While writing the book, Priestley improved his own understanding of electricity by repeating many of the experiments he described in it. He included in his history the original version of Franklin's kite experiment.

In 1767, the year the history was published, Priestley became interested in gases, or "airs," as he called them, and in this field of chemistry he made his greatest scientific discovery when he produced a comparatively pure form of oxygen in 1774. Electricity was used in some of his experiments. In 1781, for example, he produced water by releasing an electric discharge in a mixture of hydrogen and oxygen. He also established the fact that charcoal was an electrical conductor.

During the French Revolution, Priestley openly sympathized with the republicans, who repaid his support by making him a citizen of the French Republic. His views were less popular in England; in 1791 an angry mob attacked his property and destroyed his valuable collection of historic apparatus and books in Birmingham. He escaped with his life and shortly afterward migrated to the United States, where he spent his remaining years.

Henry Cavendish (1731–1810) had a very different background and character than Priestley. Born into one of the richest families in England, he was a quiet, lonely man who never married and who devoted most of his time to scientific experiments. Like Priestley, he was a pioneer in the study of gases. After discovering hydrogen he demonstrated the composition of water by burning hydrogen in air and producing an amount of water equal to the weight of the oxygen and hydrogen employed. In 1787, before a Royal Society audience, he produced nitric acid by exposing a mixture of oxygen and nitrogen to a continuous electrical discharge.

Cavendish took an active interest in electrical theory as well as chemical problems. In the controversy over pointed or blunt lightning conductors, he strongly supported points. More important than that, he undertook many electrical experiments, including a long series to test the electrical conductivity of different substances. In testing water he found that the addition of one part of salt to one part of rain water increased its conductivity one hundred times. He found, too, that a column of water 1 inch long offers as much resistance to the passage of electricity as does an iron wire of the same diameter 400,000,000 inches long.

While investigating the capacities of a condenser constructed with different dielectric substances, Cavendish discovered that glass, wax, rosin, and shellac gave higher values than air. He used the term Specific Inductive Capacity and worked out a rating scale for these substances which indicated how they compared with each other as inductors, adopting the value for air as one. However, this information was not generally known to science until half a century later when Faraday independently repeated the work. Cavendish also established but did not publicize the inverse square law of electrical attraction and repulsion which the French scientist Coulomb proved ten years later. This law states that the force of electrical attraction or repulsion is proportional to the product of the charges on the objects involved and inversely proportional to the distance between the objects.

Cavendish's scientific work was distinguished by the thoroughness of his methods and the accuracy of his results. He kept detailed notes on his investigations, but many of his records, particularly on electrical subjects, were not made known until a century had passed.

Science is closely involved with measurements. Its progress depends on the provision of instruments for measuring different quantities and on the establishment of laws connecting these quantities. So it was with the state of electrical knowledge in the later part of the eighteenth century. Although a great variety of electrical phenomena had been observed, there was still no means for measuring electrical forces precisely. Rough electrometers were used in which a suspended pith ball was repelled by a fixed electrified body. As the ball was repelled, it swung across the face of a vertical quadrant scale which measured in degrees the arc of its movement away from the charge. However, the angle of swing that the scale measured was not a true indication of the repulsive force, for well-known trigonometrical reasons: As the supporting thread became less vertical the weight of the ball had an increased controlling effect and so reduced the sensitivity of the instrument.

The first accurate measure of electrical force was devised by a French physicist, Charles Augustin Coulomb (1736–1806). Coulomb studied science in Paris and took a technical commission in the French Army. At the age of forty he retired and gave his time to scientific research. When the French Revolution broke out fifteen years after his retirement, he avoided involvement and moved to a quiet retreat near Blois.

Soon after he left the army, Coulomb developed his famous torsion balance, which was the first sensitive and reliable instrument for measuring electrical force. One of the main features of the torsion balance was a light horizontal bar carrying a ball at each end and suspended from the center by a fine thread or wire. When a ball on the bar was exposed to a similarly charged body, the force of its repulsion was measured by means of the twist produced in the suspending wire as the ball swung away. To calibrate this instrument,

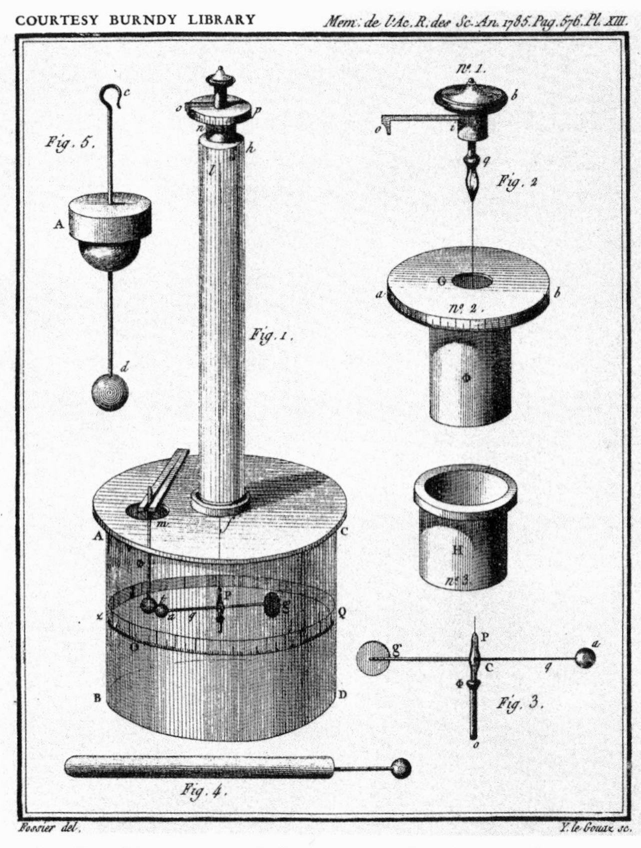

Coulomb's torsion balance was the first indicating instrument that could measure electrical charge.

Coulomb studied the laws governing the twisting of wire—that is, the relation between the force exerted and the twist produced in different kinds of wire. By careful study, he was able to determine absolute values for his electrical measurements. Using a light needle made of straw covered with sealing wax and supported by a long silken thread, he achieved a sensitivity of one hundred-thousandth of an English grain (7000 grains = 1 pound) for each degree of the circle of torsion (twist).

Coulomb was also interested in problems of mechanical friction and the viscosity of liquids, but it was his torsion balance which gave him a name in electrical science. With this device he carried out many electrical experiments and opened up completely new opportunities for electrical research.

2

LUIGI GALVANI
1737-1798

In 1786 Luigi Galvani, a professor of anatomy at the University of Bologna, noticed that the leg muscles of a dissected frog contracted when a nearby electrical machine was operated. This accidental observation opened up an area of investigation that led, through the later discoveries of Alessandro Volta, to the production of the first steady electric current.

People who are not very familiar with the work of Galvani and Volta sometimes confuse the scientific contributions made by these two men. However, their fields of interest and their approaches to research were very different, and their opposing views became a matter of public controversy. As an anatomist, Galvani was intensely interested in animal electricity and tended to give observed facts an interpretation that suited his theories. Volta, on the other hand, was a physicist who was not very interested in animals as a source of electricity and insisted on investigating electrical cause and effect apart from such a particular subject as animal tissue. Moreover, he had strong supporting evidence for his own views even in Galvani's experimental results.

Luigi Galvani was born in Bologna of an old and distin-

LUIGI GALVANI

guished family that included several members who held important positions in theology and law. As a boy he spent some time in a religious convent, and evidently found his life there satisfying, for he decided to join the order himself. Fortunately for science, one of the religious fathers convinced him that he was not sufficiently mature to make such a decision and he took up the study of medicine instead. However, he retained a religious outlook and in later life he customarily ended scientific lectures by extolling the virtues of Divine Providence to his audiences.

At the University of Bologna where Galvani studied, one of the members of the medical faculty was Professor Domenico Galeazzi, who held the university's chair of natural philosophy for forty years. Galeazzi took a special interest in Galvani, and the young medical student was welcomed regularly into the professor's home.

Galeazzi had an attractive daughter, Lucia, who had been trained in medical research at the University and shared the interests of her father and Galvani. Galvani soon fell in love with Lucia and married her in 1760. They made their home with the professor and the three of them established an informal local academy, naming themselves "The Inexperienced." In a private laboratory in their home they carried out experiments until Galeazzi's death in 1775. Working together, they made many important discoveries which provided material for over twenty papers contributed by Galeazzi to the *Commentarii*, published by the Bologna Academy of Science.

Galvani, always of a retiring disposition, was more reluctant to publish than his father-in-law. However, he recorded his observations very fully and systematically, and they appeared some fifty years later in a volume of collected works. His reluctance to publish may have been modesty or it may have been a fear of criticism, for he once remarked, "It often happens that things pleasing and acceptable when heard by word of mouth are condemned and resisted when read in print."

One of the few of Galvani's papers published during his early career was his doctoral thesis on the human skeleton and the formation and development of bone. This first essay was written in 1762 when he was twenty-five. Beginning at this time he lectured on medicine at the University of Bologna. Five years later he became custodian of the Anatomical Museum. This appointment led, in 1775, to a professorship of anatomy and, soon after, to the chair of obstetrics.

As he continued his university work in anatomy and physiology, Galvani gradually became interested in investigating muscular reactions to nerve stimulation. His interest led to the famous frog's legs incident already mentioned, which in turn launched his experiments involving the electrical stimulation of animal nerve and muscle. Although Galvani's experiments are famous he was not the first to note the effects of electricity on animals.

The ancient Romans and later the Abyssinians used the powerful shocks from an electric fish, the torpedo, as a form of therapeutic treatment. Early in the seventeenth century it was discovered that a South American fish, *Gymnotus electrica,* gave similar shock to any person or animal touching it. About 1770 several scientists took up the study of this phenomenon, and soon the electrical basis of such fish-produced shocks was generally accepted. Priestley, the English chemist, came to the conclusion that other living creatures possessed similar "animal spirits," and many experimenters took up the hunt for evidence of animal electricity. Not all the published reports of such evidence could be taken at face value, however. A professor of anatomy at Naples, for example, claimed to have received a violent shock from a mouse when he held it by the thumb and finger and made an incision of the skin.

When the invention of the frictional machine provided a source of static electricity to carry out experiments, scientists began to investigate the reverse phenomenon—the effect of electricity on animals. Even without the use of a frictional machine a Dutch naturalist, Jan Swammerdam, carried out a series of experiments in 1678 in which he produced the contraction of a muscle by withdrawing the muscle and connecting nerve from a surrounding copper ring by a silver thread.

When the Leyden jar came into use the possibility of curing paralysis by the application of shocks attracted wide attention and many experiments were carried out on living animals. In 1753, while Galvani was still a boy, Giovanni Battista Beccaria (1716–1781), a professor of physics at Turin University, found that the exposed muscles of a living rooster responded to an electric discharge. In 1756 Leopoldo Marco Antonio Caldani, Galvani's predecessor in the chair of obstetrics at Bologna, read a paper describing how he had stimulated a frog's nerve-muscle combination. In 1781, about five years before Galvani's historic laboratory incident, Felice Fontana stated that experiments must be carried out to decide whether there is an electrical principle involved in the contraction of muscles. He finished with an exclamation: "How many things are left in an uncertain state, to posterity!" Galvani was soon to play a significant part in clearing up some of the questions that Fontana had in mind.

Galvani told of his discoveries in 1791, in his famous Latin dissertation, *De Viribus Electricitatis in moto musculari commentarius* (The Effects of Animal Electricity on Muscular Motion). A classic, the work has appeared in many editions and translations. It summarizes Galvani's series of experiments in four parts. Part I deals with the effects of "artificial" (man-made) electricity on nerves and muscles. Part II describes the use of atmospheric electricity for the purpose. Part III attempts to establish "animal electricity," and Part IV consists of conjectures and conclusions regarding animal electricity.

Early in his report, Galvani tells of how he first came to notice the reaction of a dissected frog's legs to the operation of an electric machine. On September 26, 1786, a pair of frog's legs, still attached by the sciatic nerve to the vertebral column of the animal, lay on a table in Galvani's laboratory. Nearby in the room there was a frictional machine that was being used from time to time for experiments that had no connection with the dissection of the frog. It happened that an assistant of Galvani, perhaps his nephew, Giovanni Aldini, chanced to touch the frog's nerve with the point of a scalpel, and immediately all the muscles of the legs contracted in violent convulsion. As the scalpel was reapplied to the nerve it was observed that the reaction seemed to occur only if the contact was made while the frictional machine was discharging sparks.

Galvani's attention was called to this strange effect and his curiosity was aroused. He repeated the experiment many times, applying the point of the scalpel to different parts of the nerve while one of his assistants produced sparks from the frictional machine. Suspecting that the frog's muscles might be reacting to a mechanical stimulus caused by the point of the scalpel, he used the instrument on several different sets of frog's legs while the machine was not sparking, and not once was he able to produce any movement in the legs. As he continued the tests, he discovered that even when the machine was sparking, the touch of the scalpel on the frog's nerve did not always cause the muscular convulsions. He eventually traced this discrepancy to the scalpel itself, which had a bone handle attached by rivets to the blade. He observed that when the scalpel was held by the bone part it did not cause the convulsions, but when he applied it to the frog's nerve while his hand was in contact with the metal

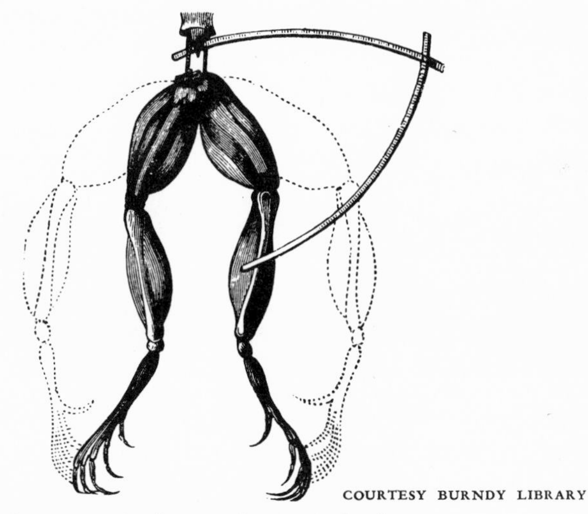

COURTESY BURNDY LIBRARY

Galvani noticed twitching in the legs of a dissected frog that was hung on an iron railing by copper hooks. He thought that this movement was due to "animal electricity."

blade or a rivet, muscular contractions were consistently produced if the electric machine was sparking.

Galvani quickly arrived at the correct explanation for what he had observed. The convulsions were produced when an electric charge induced in the dissected frog by the machine was allowed to escape. To achieve this result it was necessary to provide a circuit to pass the electricity from frog to scalpel and through the body of the experimenter to the ground. To test this conclusion, Galvani repeated the experiment, arranging the ground connections and frog's legs in a variety of ways. To determine whether the force of electricity spread out in all directions he attached frogs' legs to door hinges in all parts of the house and arranged a circuit so that all of them jumped in unison. For the ultimate experiment of this group, he set up a series of nerve conductors in a circle around the frictional machine and some distance away from it. To each of these nerves he attached a prepared frog's leg with feet touching the ground. When the machine was operated he was rewarded with the sight of all the legs jumping together.

Galvani then carried his experimentation a step further. He placed frogs' legs and a simple electrometer in a glass tube near an electrostatic machine. Although there was no connection between the machine and the tube the legs contracted and the electrometer vanes separated momentarily every time an electrostatic spark was produced.

By thus demonstrating that electricity could travel in space, Galvani had established the principle of radio transmission. However, he was not aware of the implications of his discovery, nor was any other scientist for the next century and a half.

During this stage of his researches, Galvani tried similar experiments on warm-blooded animals, including chickens and sheep. These experiments are reported in the conclusion of Part I of his dissertation.

At the time Galvani began his famous project, more than three decades had elapsed since experimenters had proved the electrical nature of thunderclouds. Atmospheric electricity had become a subject of great popular interest, and Galvani eventually decided to try its effects. In the open air he set up a vertical iron rod which he insulated from the ground. Then, using experimental preparations of frogs' legs, he attached the nerves to the lower end of the rod and placed the feet touching a wire that extended down to water in a well.

During the first thunderstorm the muscles contracted violently as soon as lightning flashed and even before the thunder was heard. Galvani noticed that the convulsions occurred not only when the nerve was in contact with the rod but also when nerve and rod were separated by a small gap. He also observed that the passing of a thundercloud caused muscular contractions although no lightning flash was evident. From experiments of this kind, he concluded that artificially created electricity and atmospheric electricity act upon animal tissue in the same way.

While he was performing these experiments, Galvani sometimes fastened the preparations of frogs' legs by metal hooks in their spinal cords to an iron railing that surrounded a hanging garden at his home. One day during a thunderstorm he noticed that the legs were contracting from time to time although the lightning rod was not in place to collect electricity. More puzzling still, he saw that the legs jumped now and then in perfectly calm weather under a clear sky. Observing these unexplained convulsions, he launched a fresh series of experiments to see if he could find a reason for the twitching. After days of waiting for its recurrence he decided that it must be produced by some factor which was eluding him. Gradually he began to suspect that there was a correlation between these infrequent twitchings and the pressure of the legs on the iron railings. During this period he wrote, "In experimenting it is easy to be deceived and to think we have seen and detected things which we wish to see and detect." To eliminate atmospheric factors as a source of electricity, he took the frogs indoors. Placing them on an iron plate, he began to press the hook fastened to the backbone against the plate. To his astonishment the legs contracted without most of the conditions that had been present in earlier experiments, that is, without a scalpel or electric machine and without atmospheric electricity. However, a person with a modern knowledge of electricity would recognize the importance of one condition that did exist. The hook was made of copper!

Galvani tried many variations of this test and was successful in producing muscular reactions. For this work, he had a willing assistant—a Spanish scholar who was then enjoying a country holiday with him—and the two of them must have had a most amusing time. In one experiment Galvani held a frog by the hook fastened to its spinal cord so that the feet touched the top of a silver box. Using the other hand he touched the box with a metal rod and the dead frog danced. He then had his young friend hold the frog while he tapped the box again, but this time nothing happened. However, when the two of them joined their free hands together while Galvani tapped the box the frog reacted violently. They had completed a circuit. A further development of this test produced what became known as Galvani's pendulum: when the frog was suspended by one leg while the other hung down and touched a silver plate, the lower leg began to oscillate up and down. The leg rose from the plate, fell when out of contact, and rose again immediately after contacting the plate.

At this stage, Galvani began to note the significance of dissimilar metals as a condition to stimulate the muscular contractions. He observed that if the hook and the lower plate were both made of iron the effect, if any, was small. If one was of iron or copper and the other of silver, the contractions were greater and lasted longer. The conclusion he drew from these observations seems incredible from our advantage of hindsight. He postulated that there was a nerve fluid or electric fire originating in the animal. As time passed, his postulation became his firm conviction that all the effects which he had observed were due to "animal electricity." His insistence on animal electricity to account for all the phenomena he had observed led to the fierce controversy between Galvani and Alessandro Volta, between the universities of Bologna and Padua (now Padova), and, in fact, between two opposing camps of scientists over the world.

Galvani carried out many unsuccessful experiments to prove his thesis that the electricity which was responsible for the muscular contractions had its seat in the tissues. Finally he had the idea of working on the analogy of the Leyden jar or the "Magic Square," the name given to a condenser composed of a sheet of glass with metallic surfaces applied to both sides. In imitation of this arrangement he encased a nerve in tin foil to augment the weak electrical effect which he was sure resided in the tissues, and, behold, it worked: when he applied an external metal circuit—an arc, as he called it—contractions of the muscles occurred. Thus, the case for animal electricity was strengthened and vindicated, according to Galvani, who wrote, "Now that a method had been found whereby we could successfully increase electricity of this kind we sought to discover the seat with greater eagerness and confidence."

From this time Galvani directed his energies to investigation of animal electricity, and the word "conjecture" began to appear in his reports more frequently. He became firmly convinced that he had established its existence in many parts of an animal but chiefly in the muscles and nerves. He believed that it traveled from one kind of tissue to another and would pass "in all haste" through an external arc of conductors or a series of men holding hands. He concluded that there were two kinds of animal electricity, one positive and one negative, and that they were completely separated from one another. He explained this concept by characterizing a muscle fiber as "something like a small Leyden Jar or . . . some other similar electrical body charged with a two-fold and opposite electricity . . ." and by comparing a nerve ". . . in some measure to the conductor of the jar." By this analogy, the whole muscle became comparable to a large group of Leyden jars.

In view of the vast amount of careful experimental work which went into Galvani's project of nearly twenty years, his final "conjectures" on animal electricity are a great disappointment to those who admire his patience, strength of purpose, and modesty. For some peculiar reason, he could not always see the obvious. The celebrated report in which he announced his results to the world is conspicuous by its lack of clarity. Fifty years later a German physiologist, Emil Du Bois-Reymond, summarized his theory as follows: "Animals have an electricity peculiar to themselves which is associated with the nerves and brain. The inner part of the nerve was the conductor of electricity and the outer oily layer an insulating covering. The muscle, on receiving the charge, acts like a Leyden jar, negative outside and positive inside, and the movement in contraction is occasioned by the irritation of the muscle fibers through the electrical stimulus in discharge."

With all its imperfections, Galvani's announcement aroused great interest among scientists and medical men as well as the general public. New methods of treating diseases of all kinds were promised and hope was even aroused that the dead might be brought back to life.

The publication of *De Viribus Electricitatis* was the crowning event of Galvani's life. When he presented his experiments and theories he expressed the hope that his report would provide a foundation for further research by eminent men of learning. His hope was realized more rapidly than he must have expected and probably with a very different result than he foresaw. When the dissertation appeared it was widely acclaimed, but only a few months elapsed before the validity of his main conclusions was challenged publicly.

Alessandro Volta, a professor of physics at Padua University, an expert in the electrical knowledge of the day, and a man of high scientific standing, examined Galvani's results with great care and published a criticism of his conclusions. Thus began the famous controversy in which the theory of animal electricity was attacked and defended by partisan groups over a period of several years. Galvani always insisted on his own firmly established opinions against opposing views: envy in others, created by his fame and popularity, caused him great distress. Nothing could abate his enthusiasm for instruction, however, and his patience in repeating interesting experiments and in answering the numerous questions of the crowds thronging his lectures endeared him to all.

But when the controversy arose, he was in no state of mind to defend his position against attack. In 1790, a year before his great announcement, he had suffered the death of Lucia, his wife and collaborator. Prostrated by a grief from which he never recovered, he left his defense to others.

The last years of his life brought hardship. In 1796 Napoleon Bonaparte invaded northern Italy and set up the Cisalpine Republic, which embraced Bologna. Galvani refused to take the oath of allegiance to the new regime, which was required of him as an officer of the university, and was consequently deprived of his office and stipend. Forced into retirement, he lived out his days in the house of his brother, Giacomo Galvani, and died on December 4, 1798. At the time of his death, friends had secured his reinstatement at the university, but the announcement came too late.

3
ALESSANDRO VOLTA
1745-1827

The year 1800 opened not only a new century but a new era in electrical history. It was the year when Alessandro Volta, the man whose name is the source of the word "volt," announced his discovery of the continuous electric current. Until his announcement all of the known electrical phenomena concerned static electricity and, apart from Franklin's lightning rod, man's electrical discoveries had little practical application. But when Volta produced the first continuous flow of current he put man on the track of harnessing a new kind of energy that would be used one day to perform daily miracles. Without the discovery he made, we would not be able to bring heat and light to our homes by pressing a switch, nor could we speak with people far away from us or share in the sight and sound of events taking place there.

During the century and a half since Volta first produced it, the electric current has been developed in a thousand applications and is a fundamental part of modern living. Even in his time the greatest significance of his work was recognized and he was highly honored. Today his name is still remembered and respected throughout the world, and Italy acclaims "Nostra Volta" (our Volta) as one of her greatest sons.

ALESSANDRO VOLTA

Alessandro Volta 1745–1827

Alessandro Volta was born at Como in the Italian region of Lombardy on February 18, 1745. His father, Don Filippo Volta, was from a family of minor nobility and his mother was Countess Maddalena Inzaghi. Their seventh child, Alessandro, was put in the care of a nurse while still a baby. During the first two and a half years of his life he lived with her and her husband, a maker of barometers and thermometers, in the village of Brunati in the hills above Como.

In his early childhood Volta's speech development was retarded. Even at the age of four he had not yet spoken a single word and his use of language continued to be subnormal until about his seventh year. His first word on record was "no," a suitable opening statement for a person whose scientific skepticism led to a discovery that would revolutionize the world.

Once Volta had overcome his early speech trouble, he progressed rapidly in school and was considered one of the brightest pupils. At the age of fifteen he entered the Jesuit college at Como where he studied philosophy. As a schoolboy he was already applying himself seriously to scientific studies. In acquiring the books and apparatus to pursue this interest he received considerable help from a wealthy young aristocrat, Cesare Gattoni, with whom he formed a strong friendship in his late teens. Gattoni's assistance must have been very welcome to Volta, for, according to his own account, his father had spent the family fortune and run into debt.

When he was a young man Volta wrote poetry and his choice of subjects showed a wide range of interests. One of his poems, for example, celebrated the conquest of Mont Blanc by Horace Bénédict de Saussure, a Swiss mountaineer-physicist. He also wrote an ode on inoculation against smallpox and a poem in Latin hexameter on the subject of such scientific discoveries of his time as the "Will o' the Wisp" or marsh gas phenomenon. His favorite theme, poetic or otherwise, was electrical science. At eighteen he wrote a letter to the celebrated physicist Abbé Nollet in which he explained his ideas on certain electrical phenomena and proposed that electrical attraction followed Newton's laws of gravitational forces. Nollet showed greater kindness in his reply to young Volta than in debating electrical theories with such acknowledged authorities as Benjamin Franklin; he wrote that he marveled at Volta's theory regarding electricity and Newton's laws but feared that it would be difficult to prove. If Volta dared to try and succeeded, he stated, the glory would be all his.

The first of Volta's scientific papers was his "De Vi Attractiva Ignis Electrici" (on the attractive force of electricity), which he addressed to the celebrated physics professor Giovanni Beccaria at the University of Turin. In the paper he displayed considerable self-confidence for a young man of twenty-four by offering to support Beccaria in opposing the double-fluid theory of electricity. At the time the double-fluid theory was being advocated by an English scientist, Robert Symmer, against the opposition of Benjamin Franklin. As proof for the theory, Symmer used a test that involved wearing two pairs of silk stockings, one black and one white. According to him, when he took them off they swelled out to the shape of his leg, and two of the same color repelled one another while two of an opposite color attracted one another. By declining to accept this evidence as favorable to the double-fluid theory, Volta secured the approval of Franklin, a much older man. A correspondence started between them, and years later they met in Paris. Considering Volta's high opinion of Franklin, Luigi Galvani could have felt greatly complimented when Volta in his assumptions on animal electricity compared the significance of Galvani's discoveries with Franklin's identification of lightning.

From his twenties Volta was very interested in the chemistry of marsh gas, which is created by the decay of animal and vegetable matter in swampy areas and now identified as methane (CH_4). After finding that the gas was inflammable he invented an electric pistol, which he used to explode samples of the mixture. This device released a spark from a Leyden jar discharge within a bottle containing the gas. In this way the explosion could be controlled while none of the products of combustion was lost. The analysis of the end products of such combustions helped to discredit a seventeenth-century theory which maintained that all inflammable materials contained an undetectable substance called phlogiston which was given off in burning. Another outcome of these experiments was Volta's eudiometer, an instrument that was afterward used to establish the proportion in which oxygen and hydrogen combined to form water.

In 1774 Volta's growing reputation as an experimental physicist prompted the governor of Lombardy to nominate him for a post as head of the physics department at the Royal School in Como. After holding the post for three years, Volta resigned to take the chair of physics at Pavia University, and he remained at Pavia until he retired forty years later.

While still at Como, Volta invented the electrophorus, an instrument which could produce an inexhaustible quantity of static electricity by induction. By the induction method, an electrified body influences an uncharged object to become charged, without any transfer of electricity between the two bodies. For several decades before the electrophorus, scientists, including Stephen Gray and Benjamin Franklin, had been aware of the possibility of inducing a charge of electricity on an object by bringing a charged body into its vicinity but not into contact. An interesting book of Italian biographies published a hundred years ago suggested that Volta got the idea for his electrophorus from reports of a Chinese discovery that electric charges could be influenced on bodies without contact. According to the book, missionaries from Peking brought reports of the discovery back to Europe in about 1755.

The electrophorus consists of a circular metal plate covered by a layer of resinous substance. A second metal plate of smaller diameter is fitted with an insulating handle in the center by which it can be lowered onto the cake of resin or taken away without the loss of any charge it may possess. In operation, the resin is rubbed or struck by a dry silken scarf or a piece of warm fur or flannel, which produces a charge on its surface. The smaller plate is then lowered by its insulating handle onto the resin, and after it is in place the operator briefly touches the top of the second plate to draw off the charge on its upper surface. When this is accomplished the small plate is lifted off the resin by its handle, and the charge on its lower surface can be carried away and transferred to another body. The operation may be repeated any number of times without diminishing the original charge on the resin plate.

The explanation for the action of the electrophorus is

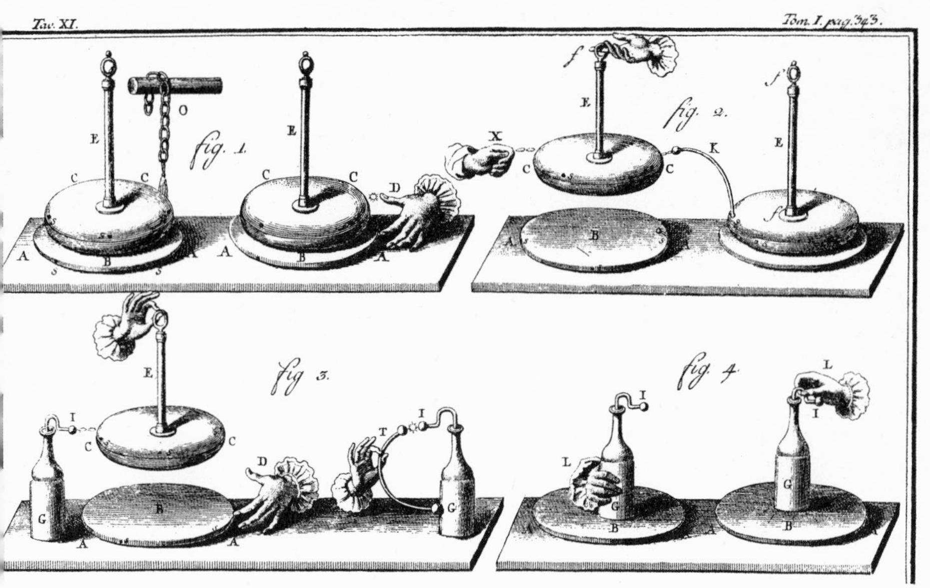

COURTESY BURNDY LIBRARY

Volta's electrophorus was an early condenser whose charge could be drawn off as needed.

fairly simple. When the uncharged plate is laid on the resin, the charge on the latter causes the positive and negative electricity already present on the upper plate to separate. A charge of opposite polarity from the resin is attracted to the lower surface of the plate and an equal charge of the same polarity as the resin is repelled to the upper surface. The repelled charge on the upper surface escapes through the touch of the experimenter, but the lower surface charge is still held by attraction. When the plate is lifted, the charge on the lower surface spreads throughout the plate and, thus trapped, can be carried away. One small but important point, probably not appreciated by Volta, explains why the electrified resin does not lose its charge *by contact* when the upper plate is set upon it. The contact between the two bodies is more apparent than real. In fact, only a few raised points on the rough surface of the resin actually touch the upper plate and, owing to the high insulating properties of the resin, its main charge cannot travel to these points.

Volta published detailed descriptions of the electrophorus which aroused much interest in scientific circles, including the Royal Society of London. The instrument became a fashionable toy and some were constructed with discs 6 and 7 feet in diameter. A model of mammouth size was made especially for Catherine the Great, then empress of Russia.

One of the scientific applications of the electrophorus was the development by Volta of a condenser for multiplying the sensitivity of electrometers. This device depended on the fact that if a condenser is made in the shape of an electrophorus, it has a high capacitance (capacity for collecting an electric charge) when the plates are close together, but a low capacitance when they are separated. When an electrometer with such a condenser connected to it is charged, the greater part of the charge at first flows to the condenser. After the source of the charge, which may be a very weak one, is disconnected and the condenser plates are separated, the accumulated charge in the condenser strengthens that in the electrometer. By taking advantage of this multiplying effect, Volta was able to perform tests using such low electrical potentials that they would not otherwise have been detected. One of his own applications of this sensitive electrometer was in the measurement of the charge induced by a passing cloud. The use of the instrument spread rapidly and provided a valuable tool in laboratories.

Beginning in his early thirties Volta took many trips out

of his homeland to visit scientists in other parts of Europe. At Aiguebelle near Geneva he observed the successful cultivation of potatoes brought over from the Argentine. To encourage the farmers in his own locality to renew their efforts at cultivating this important vegetable, he took some back to Como. In 1782 he spent several months in Paris, where he met Benjamin Franklin as well as many European scientists and participated in festivities at the court of Louis XVI and Marie Antoinette. From Paris he went to London, where a paper he had written on his electrophorus was read before the Royal Society. On this and other visits to the capitals of Europe he was received by royalty and honored by scientific societies. On a later visit to London he was made a Fellow of the Royal Society of London.

When Galvani's famous work on animal electricity was published in 1791 he sent a complimentary copy to Volta. At the time Volta was conducting research on gases, but when he read the paper he was so impressed that he immediately dropped this work to follow up Galvani's research. He studied all Galvani's results carefully and became so absorbed in the subject that he repeated Galvani's tests and checked his results, one by one.

As was his practice in all his experimental work, Volta made copious notes and wrote letters giving his results and impressions to university colleagues and other scientists in different parts of Europe. These writings indicate that Volta at first agreed with Galvani's conclusions—he accepted animal electricity as an explanation for the otherwise unexplained convulsions of Galvani's frog's legs. Even when he began to doubt Galvani's main premise, he gave him credit for his scientific contribution. In a letter written in 1792 to a scientist friend, Tiberius Cavallo in London, he stated that Galvani's work included one of the greatest and most brilliant discoveries ever made, containing the germ of many others. However, Volta also recognized Galvani's inferiority in the field of physics. On one occasion he expressed surprise that Galvani should have been ignorant of the fact that a Leyden jar could be charged in either direction, that is, with the charge on the knob either positive or negative. He also suggested that Galvani need not have been so astonished by the phenomenon of the frog's-leg contractions since the effect of electric shock on animal tissue was already well known.

While Volta was collecting the experimental data that caused him to challenge Galvani's theory, Don Bassano Carminati, a professor of medicine at Pavia, wrote to Galvani giving him details of Volta's activities. Although Carminati seemed to think he was rendering a service to both men, his letter helped to precipitate the bitter Volta-Galvani controversy. The correspondence does serve to throw light on the methods used by Volta; after detailing the results obtained by Volta that merely repeated those of Galvani, Carminati goes on to say, "But the illustrious Signor Volta wished to determine and to reduce to grades and measure, the force of electricity required in all these cases to excite in the muscles the contraction and movements described by you. He has found then that for the frog whole and alive there suffices a barely scintillating quantity of electricity, if we place the frog in the circuit of the discharge."

In the same letter Carminati related how Volta had made an "armature," as it was called, by wrapping a frog's nerve with metal foil. When the reaction of this armature was tested with a delicate Cavallo electrometer Volta found that the amount of electricity which moved the electrometer less than one-tenth of a degree was sufficient to produce the characteristic muscular contractions. "Mr. Volta," Carminati wrote, "by using his new device of increasing the sensitivity of an electrometer by the method of sharing the charge with a condenser, has proved that the frog's legs are more sensitive in detecting electricity than any known electrometer." Carminati did not know, nor did anyone else then, that Galvani himself in 1786 had made the same observation. It was recorded in his laboratory notes which were not published until 1841.

In 1794 Volta definitely abandoned Galvani's conclusion that animal electricity could have produced all the muscular contractions observed when no known electrical source was present. He offered instead a hypothesis of his own to identify the real source of the unexplained electricity. He proposed that it was to be found in the dissimilar metals used in the arc by which Galvani normally completed the circuit to produce muscular contraction.

In his memoranda, Volta described many experiments that challenged Galvani's hypothesis and gave support to his own. To test Galvani's belief that the muscular contractions might have resulted from the electrical interaction of a frog's muscle and nerve, he produced muscular twitching when a nerve was not attached. The effect was triggered with a discharge from a Leyden jar and also with electricity obtained by bringing together plates of dissimilar metals such as copper and silver. In his investigations of the effects of dissimilar metals on each other, Volta reintroduced a forgotten experiment carried out by a Swiss physicist, Johann

C. Sulzer, forty years earlier. In this test the experimenter places a strip of one metal under his tongue or in the cheek and a second strip of different metal on the tongue. When the outer ends of the strips are brought together there is a sensation of taste which does not exist when they are kept apart. In trying this experiment Volta noticed a difference in the taste of the two metals. He found that he was able to distinguish which was positively charged and which negatively and thus to determine the direction of the current. In a variation of the experiment he connected the metal strips to his forehead and palate and noted the flash of light in his closed eyes when the circuit was completed. Later he tried the same test on a dead calf and the tongue responded to the bimetallic current.

While Volta emphasized that the muscular convulsions observed in Galvani's experiments and his own could not be explained by animal electricity he did admit the possibility of its existence in letters to his friend Signor Ab. Tommasello and to Dr. Van Marum in Holland. After explaining how electric force could be generated by the application of a bimetallic strip to a moist substance he concluded that the only contractions Galvani could claim for animal electricity were the weak reactions he observed when no arc of one single metal was employed. He also believed sufficiently in animal electricity to describe a possible mechanism by which an animal could generate it in the nerves to cause a reaction in the muscles.

Volta's controversy with Galvani brought him into conflict with Giovanni Aldini, the nephew and collaborator of Galvani. Aldini, who later became professor of physics at the University of Bologna, was a young man of dynamic personality who acted as a vigorous defender of his uncle. When, in 1794, Galvani issued "Dell' Arco Electricitatis" (On the Electric Arc) as an anonymous reply to some of Volta's statements, Aldini added a many-paged supplement to Galvani's own defense. After that, Volta and Aldini were the chief protagonists in a battle that engaged the universities of Pavia and Padua, which aligned themselves with Volta, and Bologna, which sided with Galvani.

It has been suggested that Aldini was little better than a showman. While it is true that he had not received formal training in medicine, his extensive communications indicate that he was a courageous and capable experimenter. His experiments with frogs' legs demonstrated that there existed a small but quite definite amount of animal electricity that could not be attributed to any other source.

In his experiments with Galvanism—for that name was now a widely accepted electrical term—Aldini was soon producing muscular contraction in animals at Bologna, Paris, and London. Using the severed heads of oxen, sheep, and chickens he passed an electric discharge from the ears and nostrils to the tongues and found that he could make the eyes open and roll in a remarkable semblance of life. The ears also moved on these heads and the noses twitched. In one of Aldini's experiments on the decapitated body of an ox the convulsions of the legs were so violent that spectators were terrified and rapidly withdrew to safety in case it might rise to its feet. He made dead dogs grind their teeth and roll their eyes: "If reason did not curb imagination one would almost think the animal had been restored to suffering and brought back to life."

One of the scientific precautions which Aldini took was

to insure that these effects could not be attributed to physical abnormalities in the animal. He therefore confined his tests to the bodies of creatures that had been in a healthy condition before death. To make tests on human cadavers he sought the cooperation of the authorities who turned over to him the bodies of several executed criminals. He tells of such experiments conducted in Paris and London in his comprehensive "Essai sur le Galvanisme" (Essay on Galvanism), published in London in 1804. Often they were held as extensive demonstrations in hospitals and hired halls, so zealous was Aldini to publicize the tests.

The effects of the human experiments were dramatic and horrible. The arms and legs of the corpses were made to move as though lifting weights or walking. One of the tests, performed on January 17, 1803, employed the body of an executed murderer at Newgate prison. In his *Bibliographical History of Electricity and Magnetism* Paul F. Mottelay records the event as follows: "After the body had lain for an hour exposed in the cold it was handed over to the President of the London College of Surgeons who co-operated with Aldini in making numerous observations to determine the effect of galvanism with a voltaic column of one hundred and twenty copper and zinc couples." In this test Aldini used a new source of electricity discovered by Volta, and it is necessary to go back six years to see how it had become available.

As the famous controversy dragged on, Volta gradually turned away from the physiological side of Galvani's findings—that is, the reaction of animal tissue. More and more he concentrated on the physical aspects—the role of inorganic materials and forces in the phenomena that Galvani's work had brought to light. He took a physicist's approach to this research, using measuring apparatus that he continued to improve. Of great value in his experiments was his condensing electrometer, which had increased the sensitivity of voltage measurement a hundred times. His investigations now led him into combining "primary" conductors, as he called them, such as silver, copper, and zinc, with secondary conductors and checking the results of this coupling. In August 1796 he made a significant step toward the crowning discovery of his life, the pile. He measured directly the *virtu matrice* or, as we now call it, the electromotive force given by a bimetallic couple. His thoughts turned then to the problems of multiplying the effect of a single metallic pair and of constructing a device to produce an increased charge. After further experimentation he assembled several pairs of zinc and copper discs with a moist substance such as paper or flannel interleaved to separate the pairs. He found that

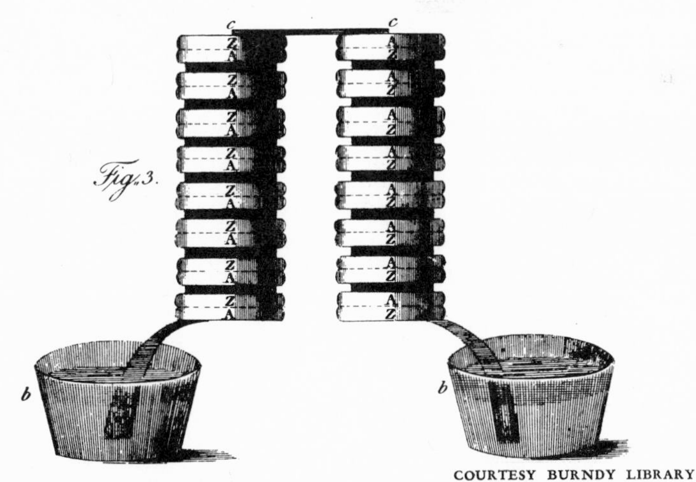

COURTESY BURNDY LIBRARY

In the voltaic pile, layers of different metallic disks separated by layers of moist pads gave out a continuous, steady electrical current.

when his electrometer was connected between the bottom and upper discs it registered a charge that increased in direct relation to the number of pairs that were in the pile. For one experiment he built up forty pairs in this way and touched the upper and lower discs so that the current flowed through his body. When his contact with the discs completed the circuit he received a shock in his hands and arms which was weaker than could be received from a fresh torpedo fish or a fully charged Leyden jar.

Volta discovered that different metals could be arranged in a definite potential series, one end having negative polarity or low potential, and the other positive polarity. This was the origin of the voltaic series, a fundamental factor in electrochemistry. To his great delight he found that the pile, as distinct from the Leyden jar, gave a continuous electrical output and not an instantaneous spark discharge.

At the end of eight years of intense thought and inspired experimentation Volta produced the first source of steady continuous electric current. Within a few months he improved his pile by producing an assembly that became famous as the *couronne des tasses* ("crown of cups"). In this assembly a series of cups containing liquid replaced the moist separator, and the bimetallic strips, formed into inverted U-shaped connections, joined one cup or cell with the next.

In 1800 Volta announced his discovery in a two-part letter written in French to the president of the Royal Society of London. The letter, which arrived in England in two sections, was read in its entirety before the Society on June 26. The following is an extract: "Yes, the apparatus of which I am telling you and which will doubtless astonish you, is nothing but a collection of good conductors of different kinds arranged in a certain manner. 30, 40, 60 pieces or more of copper, or better, of silver, each laid upon a piece of tin, or what is much better, zinc, and an equal number of layers of water, or of some other humor which is a better conductor than plain water, such as salt water, lye, etc., or pieces of cardboard, leather, etc., well soaked with these humors; such layers interposed between each couple or combination of different metals, such as alternative succession, and always in the same order, of these three kinds of conductors, that is all that constitutes my new instrument: which imitates, as I have said, the effects of Leyden Jars, or of electric batteries (formed of a collection of Leyden Jars) giving the same shock as they do; which, in truth, remains much below the activity of the said batteries charged to a high degree, as regards the force and noise of the explosions, the spark, and the distance over which the discharge can take place, etc., only equalling the effects of a battery charged to a very low degree, of a battery of immense capacity; but which, besides, infinitely surpassing the virtue and power of these same batteries, inasmuch as it does not need, as they do, to be charged beforehand, by means of outside electricity; and inasmuch as it is capable of giving a shock whenever it is touched, however frequently these contacts are made." He then proceeds to more detailed descriptions of the apparatus and the "most remarkable experiments carried out with the current produced by the pile."

This announcement was widely acclaimed throughout the scientific world. It won admiration not only because of the significance of his discoveries but also because of the objectivity of Volta's methods of investigation and his typically careful way of arguing his case.

In 1801 Volta was invited to Paris to deliver three lectures on his discovery to the French National Institute, which had replaced the French Academy of Sciences six years earlier, during the French Revolution. On his arrival there he was received by Napoleon Bonaparte, who asked him many questions about his researches and attended his second lecture. While Napoleon was present, Volta decomposed water with current from his pile. At the end of the lecture Napoleon and Volta spent several hours in discussion. Volta evidently produced a favorable impression because Napoleon immediately proposed that the gold medal of the Institute should be awarded to him. Later Volta was created Knight Commander of the French Legion of Honor and was presented with a purse of six thousand francs. In his own country his work was considered so important that a special committee of high-ranking scientists was appointed officially to study his results and continue the investigation further.

Volta's work on the pile, completed when he was fifty-five, was his last important scientific achievement. After 1800 he gradually withdrew from university and public affairs and occupied himself with his family, which included three young sons born of his marriage at forty-nine to Teresa Peregrini, a count's daughter. One of his sons died in 1815, but the other two completed university studies at Pavia. When they graduated in 1819 Volta took his family back to Como. He died there on March 5, 1827, at the age of eighty-two.

The passage of time has not diminished Volta's fame, particularly in his own country. At Brunati, where he spent his early days in the hills above Como, a light that is lit by Volta's current still shines nightly from a stone tower. Although much of his original apparatus was destroyed by fire years ago, there is still a collection on exhibit in the Temple Voltiana on the outskirts of Como.

4

HUMPHRY DAVY
1778-1829

After Volta announced his development of the continuous electric current, men in scientific circles everywhere began to construct their own voltaic piles and to find ways of applying the current. Foremost among them was Humphry Davy. During his comparatively short life Davy made spectacular contributions to the knowledge of chemistry and the practical use of electricity. Through his application of the new electric current to chemical compounds he advanced existing ideas on the constitution of matter and helped lay the foundations of some of our greatest industries. One of his inventions, the miner's lamp, saved thousands of lives, and another solved a serious problem for the English navy. In reaching the summit of his profession through strenuous years of lecturing and experimentation at the Royal Institution in London, he raised the prestige of that world-famous center of science and culture to an eminence that it has held for a century and a half.

Humphry Davy was born in Penzance, near the western tip of England, on December 17, 1778. Cornwall, the county of his birth and boyhood, is noted for its rugged coast, its picturesque towns, and its unusual history. The prehistoric Celts had left their stone constructions there,

HUMPHRY DAVY

and, spreading over the barren uplands, the ancient tin mines recalled the activities of the Phoenicians, who traded in Cornish tin before the Roman occupation of Britain. Now Davy himself is part of Cornwall's history. In the market place at Penzance there is a stone statue of him holding his famous miner's lamp.

Humphry Davy's father, Robert Davy, was the son of a builder and had inherited land that provided him with a small but assured income. Trained as a wood-carver, he followed his trade with some skill but with little application or profit while he occupied himself with field sports and unprofitable farming ventures. In 1776 he married Grace Millet, who gave birth to Humphry some two years later and remained very close to her famous son until she died just a few years before him. She and her two sisters had been orphaned while still quite young by the sudden death of both parents within a few days of each other. At the time a young surgeon and apothecary, John Tonkin, had been living with the Millet family and he made himself responsible for the care of the three sisters until they married. After Grace's marriage he continued to take an interest in her and her family and played an important part in the rearing and education of Humphry.

From his early childhood Davy had an exceptionally quick mind and an ability to remember what he heard or read. Even before he could read them for himself, he could recite long parts of stories from the *Arabian Nights, Aesop's Fables,* and other classics told to him by his paternal grandmother, who seems to have been a woman of some intellect. He had begun to read and write before he was five and soon was skimming through books so quickly that he might have been counting the number of pages rather than reading them. However, on being questioned, he was able to give a satisfactory account of the contents.

Humphry Davy started his formal education in a local private school and showed such ability that after a few months his teacher recommended he be sent to a better institution. Thus at the age of six he was entered at the Penzance Grammar School, presided over by the Reverend Mr. Coryton, whom Humphry's brother John later described as "of irregular habits, as deficient in good method as in sound scholarship." According to John, "Pulling the boys' ears was practiced by him in the most capricious manner and my brother was too frequently a sufferer from this infliction." For his own part, Humphry seems to have had little respect for his teacher. On one occasion he appeared in school with a large plaster on each ear. When Mr. Coryton asked him what was the matter with his ears, he replied with a grave face that he had "put the plaster on to prevent a mortification."

Under such instruction Humphry's talents did not shine. Looking back on the experience in later years he wrote that he had "enjoyed much idleness." But out of school hours his life was more stimulating. In the company of adults within the family circle and with fishermen friends on the quayside he was a lively talker. One of his great ambitions was to be an orator, and with other boys as an audience he would sometimes recite by the hour using stories and poems from his memory and imagination. When he had no audience he would shut himself in a room and lecture to the chairs. One of his favorite works was *Pilgrim's Progress*, most of which he knew by heart.

This early interest in literature and composition remained with Davy throughout his life. At seventeen he wrote a lengthy poem entitled "The Sons of Genius." In manhood he made friends with Robert Southey, Sir Walter Scott, William Wordsworth, and Samuel Coleridge, who once said that if Davy had not been the first chemist he would have been the first poet of his age.

Another lifelong interest that Davy developed in his school years was fishing. As a boy he joined his father on many fishing excursions and in later years he seized every opportunity in his crowded life to indulge in the sport. Even on his bridal tour to Scotland in 1812 he did some fishing. While traveling with his bride and his brother, who was accompanying them for part of their journey, he suddenly rode on ahead when the river Awe came in sight. By the time his companions caught up with him he was fishing.

When Davy was nine, his parents moved from Penzance. Davy, however, remained in the town under the charge of Mr. Tonkin, who, at his own expense, sent Davy as a boarder to Truro Grammar School some five years later. Davy had been at the school only one year when his father died suddenly in 1794 leaving Mrs. Davy heavily in debt and with a younger son and three daughters to support. Once again Mr. Tonkin came to the rescue. He paid sixty guineas consideration money to enable Davy to be apprenticed to a Mr. Borlase, who, like Tonkin, was a surgeon and apothecary. He also helped Mrs. Davy to establish a dressmaking business in Penzance which she managed well enough to pay off the family debts and support her children.

The loss of his father and the courageous way his mother faced this tragedy and the ensuing financial difficulties deeply affected Davy. He resolved that he must begin to take life seriously and achieve success by hard work and study. In the spirit of this resolve he began during the early years of his apprenticeship to record his thoughts in a famous series of notebooks still treasured at the Royal Institution in London, where he later worked. His first three essays were recorded under a heading he called "Hints Towards the Investigation of Truth in Religious and Political Opinions." They were separately titled "On the Immortality and Immateriality of the Soul," "Body, organized matter," and "On Governments." He also set down in the notebook verses that he had composed and the outline of a program he had worked out for himself. His major objectives were listed in the outline under ten headings: Theology, Geography, My Profession, Logic, Language, Physics, Mechanics, History and Chronology, Rhetoric and Oratory, and Mathematics. For each of these categories he listed ambitious goals. For example, it was his plan to master seven different languages, including Latin and Greek, in which he had already shown ability at Truro.

It was at this time in his life that Davy began to take up science in a serious way. In earlier years he had carried out experiments with crude equipment in Mr. Tonkin's home. His budding interest was fed when at nineteen he came across Antoine Lavoisier's classic textbook, *Traité Elémentaire de Chimie* (Elementary Treatise on Chemistry), first published in France in 1789. Although the book had been translated into English by the time Davy became aware of it, he may have read the work in the original French, for he was quite far advanced in his knowledge of the language. Nor was his reaction to the book a mere passive acceptance of Lavoisier's ideas; he carried out his own experiments and recorded some views of his own that opposed those of the great French chemist.

Among the other influences that may have led Davy in the direction of science were two men who became his friends. One was Gregory Watt, the son of the inventor of the condensing steam engine. Watt, who had studied chemistry at the University of Glasgow, came to Penzance for health reasons and made his home with the Davy family until he died five years later. During those last years of his life, he and Humphry Davy went on excursions together along the seashore and in the rocky coastal regions of Cornwall and discussed natural history and poetry. When Davy looked back on those occasions in later years he always described them with emotion.

Even more important to Davy's future career was Davies Gilbert, who was a mathematician and the sheriff of the county. Upon hearing that Davy was interested in chemical experiments, Gilbert invited the young man to his house, offered him the use of his library, and in various other ways helped to advance Davy's interests. It was Gilbert who was responsible for Davy's first view of a real chemical laboratory where "the air-pump more especially fixed his attention, and he worked with its pistons, exhausted the receiver and opened its valves, with the simplicity and joy of a child engaged in the examination of a new and favorite toy."

Through Watt and Gilbert, Davy met the man who was to take him out of the remote country town of his birth into the greater world of science and society. During his last illness Watt was being attended by a Dr. Thomas Beddoes, who had been a professor of chemistry at Oxford while Gilbert was studying there. Dr. Beddoes had lost his post at Oxford because of his support for the French Revolution, and when Davy met him he was in the process of establishing the Pneumatic Medical Institution at Clifton, near Bristol, to investigate and apply the therapeutic properties of inhaled gases.

On the recommendation of Gilbert, Davy was appointed to direct the laboratory and to assist Dr. Beddoes in publishing the experimental findings of the new institution. In order to accept the appointment Davy had to be released from his apprenticeship, and in this Dr. Borlase was very cooperative. He offered a testimonial to Davy's excellent behavior and wrote on the back of the indentures that he released Davy "because being a youth of great promise I would not obstruct his present pursuits which are likely to promote his future and his fame." Davy had a harder time with his family, however. His mother did not favor the enterprise and Mr. Tonkin thought Dr. Beddoes was a misguided charlatan. Although his mother came to accept Davy's new career, Mr. Tonkin never relented and revoked a legacy he had made in Davy's favor. Nevertheless, Davy on his twentieth birthday took the coach to Bristol, his eyes bright with the prospect of fame.

Davy's two years at the Pneumatic Institution must have been among the happiest in his life. Dr. Beddoes did not curb the young man's exuberance; on the contrary, he found that the quick and sometimes reckless brilliance of Davy's experiments and lectures were adding to the prestige of the Institution, which depended on the subscriptions of people who came from long distances and paid for treatment.

In addition to the excitement of his work, Davy was introduced into literary and fashionable circles by Mrs. Beddoes, who was a sister of the author Maria Edgeworth. Davy described his employer's wife, who was only five years his senior, as "extremely cheerful, gay and witty, one of the most pleasing women I ever met. . . ."

Through his professional and social activities Davy became acquainted with members of the Wedgwood family; Erasmus Darwin, grandfather of the celebrated naturalist Charles Darwin; Roget of thesaurus fame; and the poets Southey and Coleridge, among others. The two poets became his close friends and admirers. Southey once described him as "a miraculous man whose talents I can only wonder at." Coleridge, whose high opinion of Davy's poetic gifts has already been mentioned, was asked many years after their meeting how Davy compared with others who had been called the cleverest men. He replied, "Why Davy can eat them all. There is an energy which enables him to seize on and analyze all questions pushing them to their legitimate consequences . . . living thoughts grow like turf under his feet."

A rather unhappy side of the Clifton picture arose from Beddoes' inordinate desire for publicity and Davy's immaturity and egoism. Dr. Beddoes had arranged to publish a collection of physical and medical knowledge and agreed with Davy to include in the volume two of Davy's essays, one entitled "Heat, Light, and the Combustion of Light" and the other "On the generation of Phosoxygen [Oxygen Gas] and on the Causes of Colours of Organic Beings." A total of two hundred pages by a boy of eighteen!

This was one of Davy's most serious mistakes. As his first scientific publication and because of the reputation he had already achieved, it raised high hopes, but the results were disastrous. Mature scientific critics descended on him and declared that many of his conclusions were valueless, largely owing to the careless way in which he had carried out his experiments. Although the papers contained much of value, the general condemnation and ridicule were a serious blow to Davy. For the rest of his life the experience was one he deplored and hated to hear mentioned.

Nevertheless he was not a man to sit down under defeat. He publicly admitted his mistakes and directed his feverish energy into further experiments, which he performed with greater care to insure precise and detailed observations.

In the well-equipped laboratory of the Pneumatic Institution Davy had begun to test the effects of breathing various gases. He had many willing subjects for the experiments among his new friends, but he did not hesitate to try even the most dangerous mixtures on himself. Nitrous oxide or laughing gas was a favored subject for investigation because it had a remarkable effect on people and did not appear to harm them. In the early months of 1799 he wrote a description of one of his own experiences with nitrous oxide: "I breathed today in the presence of Dr. Beddoes and some others, sixteen quarts of it for near seven minutes. It appears to support life longer than even oxygen gas, and absolutely intoxicated me . . . this gas raised my pulse upwards of twenty strokes, made me dance about the laboratory as a madman and has kept my spirits in a glow ever since."

By such experiments Davy found that toothaches could be relieved by inhalation of nitrous oxide; he also suggested its use for surgical operations. When his discovery of the anesthetic use of the gas was announced by Dr. Beddoes the news added greatly to the fame of the Institution.

Not all the gases that Davy breathed were as pleasant as nitrous oxide. Some of them made him seriously ill, and on one occasion he almost killed himself, recovering only after a long convalescence. After this extended and sometimes dangerous series of experiments Davy published a book that restored his reputation in the eyes of his scientific contemporaries. The reference that he made in it to the use of gas in surgical operations has been claimed as the first recorded suggestion for the practice of anesthesia.

Although Davy was a chemist first and foremost he also made brilliant discoveries regarding the application of the electric current. While he was at the Pneumatic Institution he learned of Volta's pile for the production of current. He also heard of the accidental discovery by William Nicholson and Anthony Carlisle that, when two wires connected to a voltaic pile were immersed near each other in water, bubbles of gas appeared. They had identified the gas collected by one wire as hydrogen and by the other as oxygen. They also found that the volume of the hydrogen gas produced was twice that of the oxygen.

The news of these findings took Davy into a new area of investigation that became the crowning work of his career. It was at this time also that the scene of his work shifted from the Pneumatic Institution to London, where his story became involved with that of another remarkable man and a new institution that Davy would help to make famous.

The man was Benjamin Thompson, Count Rumford, whose life was one of the outstanding success stories of his time. Born in Woburn, Massachusetts, in 1753, Thompson began his career as a merchant's apprentice in Salem, Massachusetts. He took his first big step upward in the world by marrying a rich widow. Continuing to improve his connections and position, he became a friend of Governor John Wentworth at Portsmouth, New Hampshire. A few years later he traveled to London and was given the post of Undersecretary of State in England's government department responsible for conducting the war in America. By the age of twenty-six he was a Fellow of the Royal Society of London and at thirty he was knighted by George III of England. His second wife was the widow of the French scientist and nobleman, Antoine Lavoisier, who died on the guillotine during the French Revolution. In 1791 he was elected a Count of the Holy Roman Empire after he had introduced major reforms in the Bavarian army and its systems of education, agriculture, and unemployment relief. For his title he took the name of Rumford after the village in New Hampshire, now the city of Concord, where he had once served as schoolmaster.

Such was the man who in 1799 founded the Royal Institution in London "for diffusing the knowledge and facilitating the general introduction of useful mechanical inventions and improvements and for teaching by courses of philosophical lectures and experts the application of science to the common purposes of life."

Count Rumford, who had investigated improvements in firearms, may have become interested in Davy as the author of published observations regarding the heating of cannon as they were being bored in the arsenal at Munich, which was then part of the Holy Roman Empire. He was probably also aware that Davy had publicly supported his opposition to the phlogiston theory, the idea that there is a substance called phlogiston in anything that can be burned. In any case, Davy received the offer of a position from Count Rumford and wrote to his mother about it:

My dear Mother,

During the last three weeks I have been much occupied by business of a very serious nature . . . I now catch a few moments only of leisure to inform you that I am exceedingly well, and that I have had proposals of a very flattering nature to induce me to leave the Pneumatic Institution for a permanent establishment in London.

You have perhaps heard of the Royal Philosophical Institution, established by Count Rumford, and others of the aristocracy. It is a very splendid establishment, and wants only a combination of talents to render it eminently useful.

Count Rumford has made proposals to me to settle myself there with the present appointment of assistant lecturer on chemistry and experimenter to the Institute; but this only to prepare the way for my being in a short time sole professor of chemistry etc.; an appointment as honorable as any scientific appointment in the kingdom . . .

You will all, I dare say be glad to see me getting amongst the *Royalists* but I will accept of no appointment except upon the sacred terms of *independence*.

I am your affectionate son,

H. Davy.

With the good wishes of Dr. Beddoes and the promise of "a room in the house furnished with coal and candles," Davy moved to London and took up the new appointment on March 11, 1801. His first lecture, delivered six weeks later, was a survey of galvanism. Before an audience which included Sir Joseph Banks, the President of the Royal Society, Count Rumford, and other distinguished scientists, he repeated Galvani's experiments on frogs' legs and demonstrated the effects of the electric current on solutions of metals in acids. Reporting on the lecture, the *Philosophical Magazine* commented that "Mr. Davy who appeared to be very young"—he was twenty-two—"acquitted himself admirably well; from the sparkling intelligence of his eye, his animated manner and the *tout ensemble,* we have no doubt of his attaining a distinguished eminence."

Davy's early program of lectures, largely decided by the managers of the Royal Institution, included courses on the science of tanning for practical men and on agricultural science for farmers. In addition, his arrangements with the Institution allowed him to study special projects that interested him from time to time. Various accounts tell of the sensation he created by his appearance and performance at these lectures. One of them reported that "men of the first rank and talent—the literary and the scientific, the practical and the theoretical, blue stockings and women of fashion, all eagerly crowded the lecture room. His youth, his simplicity, his natural eloquence, his chemical knowledge, his happy illustrations and well-conducted experiments, excited universal attention and unbounded applause. Compliments, invitations and presents were showered on him—a talented lady, since well known in the literary world, addressed him anonymously in a poem of considerable length—it was accompanied by a handsome ornamental appendage for the watch which he was requested to wear when he delivered his next lecture as a token of having received the poem and pardoned the freedom of the writer." A literary reaction to his performance was supplied by his friend Coleridge, frequently present at the lectures, who once wrote, "I attend to increase my stock of metaphors."

Besides lecturing, Davy also experimented with the application of electric current which he produced with batteries based on Volta's ideas. At an early stage in these experiments he noticed the tiny spark that occurred when two wires connected to a battery were separated. He tried using different materials in the wire to increase this effect and found that carbon produced the most outstanding result. This led to his development of the carbon arc, which became a popular lecture subject. Even in Davy's time the arc was more than a curiosity. It became a convenient source of high-temperature heat for chemical experiments and was far in advance of anything else then available. Looking beyond Davy's time, the carbon arc was an important step in the development of electric lighting.

In his experiments with electric current Davy was particularly interested in the chemical changes brought about by applying the current. Toward the end of 1807 he started investigating the possibility of decomposing alkaline substances by electricity with results that were of major importance in the history of science.

Starting with dry potash he found he could get no current to pass through the mixture. Then he tried dissolving the potash as a strong solution in water, but still there was no decomposition of the alkali, only bubbles of hydrogen and oxygen from the water. Finally he tried a potash sample which had become damp by exposure to the air and he found a violent reaction taking place. The potash began to liquefy and small globules similar to quicksilver came to the surface. Most of these globules burst into flame on coming in contact with the air and some simply became tarnished.

Davy obtained similar results when he tried heating a damp mixture of soda to a high temperature with the electric current. He had difficulty in collecting the substances produced by this procedure because of their affinity for oxygen. After he found they could be stored in naphtha he was able to identify their properties.

In describing his discoveries before the Royal Society of London he gave the substances obtained from the breakdown of potash and soda the names potassium and sodium. He described potassium as a malleable substance with the bright appearance of silver and sodium as a white opaque substance. His announcement created a sensation and upset many previous ideas. How could potash and soda contain metals, people wondered. Some decided that Davy was "a very troublesome person in chemistry."

The long hours and intense excitement that Davy expended in making and recording these discoveries proved too much for him. Within a few days after he had completed all the work he became seriously ill. For a time it seemed that he could not recover, but he rallied and within months was back again at work in the laboratory. Calcium, strontium, barium, and magnesium were among the forty-seven elements that Davy isolated and identified. He demonstrated that chlorine was an element in spite of wide views to the contrary and gave it the name chlorine to replace "dephlogisticated spirit of salt." In many other ways he made major contributions to chemistry that are recorded in the nine volumes of his collected works, edited by his brother John in 1839. He had been elected a Fellow of the Royal Society in

Davy's electric-spark apparatus was used to test gas pressure.

1803 and, through the years, the Society published many of his papers, which have since become classics in the history of science. On April 8, 1812, Davy was knighted and three days later, at the age of thirty-four, he married.

His bride, Mrs. Apreece, was a rich young widow of Scottish descent and a remote cousin of Sir Walter Scott. A woman of considerable charm and strength of character, she had traveled widely and had a host of distinguished friends and admirers. Her capacity for sharing the interests of those she met and the fact that she enjoyed fishing were certainly among her attractions for Sir Humphry. The little bundle of Davy's letters written at this time and found after her death in 1855 show that there was mutual admiration and that Davy was convinced of her desire to share in his scientific interests. The letters are now among the most highly valued possessions of the Royal Institution.

After a prolonged bridal tour in Scotland Davy settled down to write his *Elements of Chemical Philosophy* and to further chemical investigations. The following year he resigned his position as professor of chemistry at the Royal Institution and in the autumn embarked on a continental tour. Michael Faraday, a newly appointed assistant in the laboratory, accompanied Sir Humphry and Lady Davy on this tour and kept a diary, which is a valuable record of Davy's activities until they returned to England in April 1815.

During the tour it became clear to observers that Davy's marriage was not turning out to be a complete success. Faraday's diary expresses loyalty to Davy and bitter irritation at the behavior of Lady Davy. John Davy, in writing his brother's biography, said of Humphry and his wife that "it might have been better if they had never met." Davy himself made a revealing comment in one of his letters; after referring to the bad effects of a few drops of bitter extract on the most exquisite wines, he went on, ". . . a bad temper has the same effect in life which is made up, not of great sacrifices or duties, but of little things, in which smiles and kindness and small obligations given habitually, are what win and preserve the heart and secure comfort."

In spite of any difficulties he may have been having with his marriage, Davy found a new preoccupation when he returned to England. The country had been shocked by several explosions in which hundreds of miners had been killed and Davy was requested to study the problem of replacing the open candle lamps that had fired explosive gases in the mines. He then made a tour of the mining areas and carried out a series of experiments which led him to the conclusion that flame in explosive mixtures would not pass through small openings. On the basis of his findings he constructed a series of lamps and, early in 1816, announced to the Royal Society that a form of lamp with a gauze screen had proved to be safe. Within a few months the lamp was widely adopted in mines throughout the country. Davy refused to protect the invention saying, "My sole object was to serve the cause of humanity and if I have succeeded, I am amply rewarded in the gratifying reflection of having done so."

During the next two years Davy did much traveling and discussed new scientific problems with the leading scientists in various European countries. He was elected president of the Royal Society in 1820 and held the office for seven years while still finding time for research work. His record in this position is marred by his ungenerous attitude toward Michael Faraday, his successor at the Royal Institution. At one time his jealousy led him to oppose Faraday's election to the Royal Society.

In 1823 Davy showed signs of failing health although he continued to work. At the time, the English Admiralty was worried about the corrosion of the copper sheeting applied to the wooden hulls of ships. The problem was one that had come to Davy's attention many years before in Penzance, where floodgates had corroded in a similar way. Davy had suspected that the cause was some kind of chemical action between iron and copper, for from his chemical investigations he knew that the different electric potentials assumed by various metals were a significant factor in corrosion problems. When his cooperation was sought on the ship problem he naturally became interested and quickly found a solution. He rendered the copper electronegative by connecting to it bars or "protectors" of cast iron.

Throughout his life Davy had shown a great affection for his mother and her death in 1826 seems to have contributed to his failing health. During that year his friends became alarmed at his appearance. On medical advice he took a trip to Italy with his brother John but returned little better for the change. Among the last of his writings were *Salmonia, or Days of Fly Fishing* and *Consolations in Travel.* On a final journey to the Continent he wrote many letters to friends at home and sent for his brother. John Davy and Lady Davy were both living with him on the Lake of Geneva when he died in the early morning hours of May 29, 1829.

5

HANS CHRISTIAN OERSTED
1777-1851

In the development of any science some men contribute by adding new details to the existing knowledge while others open up entirely new areas of investigation, making what is called a scientific breakthrough. This distinction is noticeable among the men who made electrical history: Volta produced the first continuous electric current, Davy explored its use, and Oersted, by establishing a definite relationship between electricity and magnetism, opened the way for further electrical discovery and application.

Hans Christian Oersted was born on August 14, 1777, in the small Danish town of Rudköbing on the Baltic Sea island of Langeland. The eldest son of a pharmacist, he was particularly close to his brother Anders, born a year later. Both developed an enthusiasm for learning and they shared their struggles to get an education. Probably their mutual encouragement helped them both to reach the heights of their professions. Hans Christian became the leading physicist of his country during his time and Anders became the prime minister of Denmark.

While the brothers were growing up in Rudköbing, their opportunities seemed very limited. There was no school in

COURTESY BURNDY LIBRARY

HANS CHRISTIAN OERSTED

town, and the family, which was growing larger, had insufficient income to send Hans and Anders away for formal schooling. However, both parents were interested in education and encouraged the children to take part in their adult conversations. Another couple in the town who took an interest in the brothers were Christian Oldenburg, a German who ran a wigmaking business, and his Danish wife. Placed under the Oldenburgs' care at an early age, Hans and Anders were taught to read in their mother tongue by Mrs. Oldenburg while Mr. Oldenburg taught them German. At the time the Danish language was in a revolutionary stage of development, with many dialects and no well-established forms of grammar and spelling, and under these circumstances the boys were particularly fortunate to be able to learn German. Not only did it give them a second language, one more widely used than their own, but it helped them acquire an exceptional mastery of Danish, which had borrowed many German words.

Besides the Oldenburgs, Hans and Anders found other teachers in the town. The baker taught them drawing; the mayor, French and English; and the local surveyor, the rudiments of mathematics. In addition to all this amateur instruction, they borrowed or bought books whenever they could.

At the age twelve, Hans entered his father's pharmacy business and thus added chemistry to his other studies. While he began to channel his interest into medicine and science, Anders concentrated on law. Both made such progress in the next few years that they decided to aim at a university course. In 1794, with their father's encouragement, they went to Copenhagen to take six months of preliminary training for the university. In the fall of that year they both easily passed the university entrance examinations. Hans chose pharmacy, astronomy, and physics as his fields of study, and Anders chose law and philosophy.

During the six years they studied at the University of Copenhagen, the brothers received a small public grant and earned extra money by private teaching. All this time they shared their money and lodgings, ate with relatives, and managed their affairs well enough to get along without further financial help from their father, who had many other children to support. Among their other mutual interests the brothers were both friends of Adam Oehlenschläger, a fellow student at the university who became a famous poet and the spiritual leader of the Danish romantic movement. Afterward Oehlenschläger's sister became Anders' wife.

Oersted never allowed his study of science to displace his interest in literature and philosophy. At the end of his first three years at the university he not only passed his pharmaceutical examinations but also won a university gold medal for an essay entitled "Limits of Poetry and Prose," a work that showed the influence of the German philosophers Friedrich von Schelling and Immanuel Kant. He later won another award for an essay on a medical subject, and his Ph.D. degree was granted in 1799 for a dissertation entitled "Architectonicks of Natural Metaphysics."

In 1800 Oersted took over the management of a pharmacy business belonging to a professor in Copenhagen who was going abroad for a year. He also replaced the professor at the university for the time, a position that made it easier for him to continue with his research work. Today the pharmacy business that he managed is still operating under the same name of Løve Apoteket (Lion Apothecaries) and at the same address, Amager 33 in Copenhagen, as in Oersted's time.

With the payment he received from his caretaker duties and a grant that the university gave him in recognition of the excellent way he had filled the professor's post, Oersted was able to finance a trip abroad. Visiting France, Germany, and Holland, he met such important philosophers as Schelling and some of the leading scientific personalities of his day, including Count Rumford and Johann Wilhelm Ritter.

Of all the contacts he made, the most valuable was Ritter, who was exploring the possibilities of Volta's electric current and had invented the first accumulator or storage battery for current. One incident that occurred when the two men met in Paris is interesting as an example of Oersted's remarkable facility in languages. Ritter, who wished to submit a paper to the French Institute on his new discovery, appealed to Oersted to translate his work from German into French. Oersted agreed and did such a good job that Ritter later declared he understood Oersted's version better than his own original work.

On his return to Copenhagen Oersted received a small allowance from the state that enabled him to spend his time in research. Even when a fire at the university destroyed the laboratory where he worked he improvised until he secured private donations for the purchase of new apparatus, and his impressive record of experiments, papers, and lectures caused the university to appoint him to a chair of physics in 1806. Three years later he published his famous *Manual of Mechanical Physics*.

In 1812 Oersted went abroad again. While in Berlin he

was persuaded by the famous German traveler Karsten Niebuhr to publish a four-page pamphlet titled "Views on the Chemical Laws of Nature." This work, later translated from German into French, established Oersted as a clear and original thinker in the electrochemical field. His ideas made a major contribution to the theory, later developed by Berzelius, Faraday, and others, that molecules were held together by electrical forces.

Oersted married in Copenhagen in 1814. He was then thirty-seven and his bride, the daughter of a pastor, was twelve years his junior. The marriage seems to have been happy and the couple reared a family of three sons and four daughters. None of the children became very distinguished although one of the daughters, Mathilde, eventually collected and published her father's letters.

At some time during the winter of 1819–20 Oersted observed the reaction of a magnetic needle to voltaic current. His observation represented the first definite proof of the relationship between magnetism and electricity, although the suspicion of such a relationship had intrigued many people for years. Navigators knew that their compass needles were weakened and could even be reversed in polarity by the effects of lightning. It had also been noted that magnetism had two polarities, as had static electricity, and that the attraction exerted both by magnets and electrically charged bodies was inversely proportional to the distance of the attracted objects. Steel knives in a kitchen box struck by lightning were found to be magnetized, and Benjamin Franklin had deliberately magnetized sewing needles by the discharge from a battery of large Leyden jars. In 1774 the Electrical Academy of Bavaria offered a prize for an essay on the subject "Is there a real and physical analogy between electric and magnetic forces . . . ?" and many years later Humphry Davy proposed to magnetize steel rods by fixing them at right angles to lightning conductors.

When Volta developed the steady current some people began to speculate about its magnetic effects. One was an Italian named Romagnosi, who published a paper in the *Gazette de Trento* in 1802 which was interpreted as "establishing the directive influence of the Galvanic current upon a magnetic needle." However, from what is known of Romagnosi's experiment, it appears that the deflection of the needle which he observed was obtained when his voltaic cell was on an open circuit with no current flowing. In that case, the needle was simply acting as an electrometer as would a similar piece of brass or other nonmagnetic metal.

All available evidence points to Oersted as the first to investigate scientifically the effects of combining Volta's pile with a magnetic needle. The exact date of his discovery proving electromagnetism and the circumstances surrounding it are somewhat obscure. It seems that at the end of the year 1819 he showed a group of his senior students that he could produce a small deflection in a magnetic needle with a wire carrying the current parallel to the needle and over it. One biographer says that he was demonstrating the heating of a platinum wire by the current and happened to lay the compass underneath the wire when he noticed the needle's deflection for the first time. It has also been suggested that an assistant was performing the experiment with the wire placed at right angles to the compass needle (which would produce no deflection) and that Oersted told him to try the effect of laying the wire over the needle and parallel with it.

This latter version of the circumstances surrounding Oersted's discovery is based on a letter written some thirty years later by a Norwegian scientist, Christian Hansteen, and addressed to the British scientist Michael Faraday. According to Hansteen, "Professor Oersted was a man of genius but he was a very unhappy experimenter; he would not manipulate instruments. He must always have an assistant or one of his auditors, who had easy hands to arrange the experiment; I have often in this way assisted him as his auditor. . . . Once, after the end of his lecture, as he had used a strong galvanic battery in other experiments he said 'Let us now once, as the battery is in activity, try to place the wire parallel with the needle.' As this was done he was quite struck with perplexity by seeing the needle making a great oscillation (almost at right angles with the magnetic meridian). Then he said 'Let us now invert the direction of the current,' and the needle deviated in the contrary direction. Thus the great detection was made; and it has been said, not without reason, that he stumbled over it by accident. He had not had before any more idea than any other person that the force should be transversal, that is, causing the needle to point crosswise from the wire. But as Lagrange said of Newton on a similar occasion, 'Such accidents only meet persons who deserve them.' "

In July 1820 Oersted described his observations in a pamphlet written in Latin and entitled "Experimenta circa effectum conflictus electrici in acum magneticum" (Experiments on the Effects of Electrical Impulses on a Magnetic Needle). Copies of it were sent to all the European learned societies, and scientists quickly recognized the significance of the discovery. His work prepared the way for a new surge of

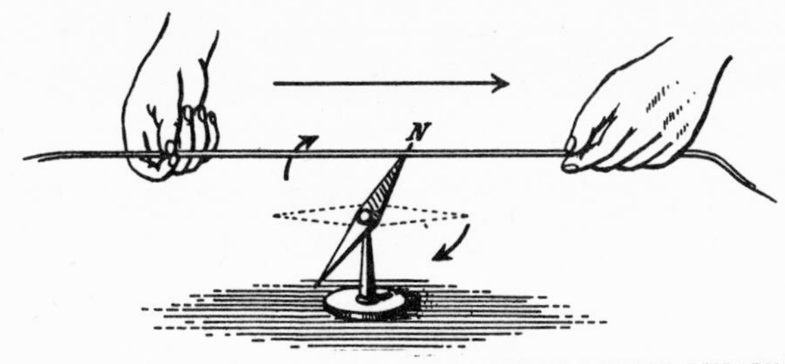

COURTESY BURNDY LIBRARY

Oersted discovered that a wire carrying a current has a circular magnetic field around it that affects an adjacent magnetic needle. This provided the first clue to the fact that magnetism and electricity were related.

electrical progress that became the stories of Ampère, Faraday, and others.

After his discovery Oersted received many honors, including the Copley Medal of the Royal Society of London and a prize of three thousand francs from the Institute of France. He paid further visits to European capitals for lectures and discussion with scientific friends. Probably his most valuable contribution during this period of his life was his effort to spread scientific knowledge among people in his country. In those days the average Dane had very little interest in the natural sciences, although literature, history, and the humanities were an important part of his general education. Oersted decided that this state of affairs should be changed and in 1824 he founded a society for the promotion of natural sciences in Denmark. Courses of popular lectures were arranged, and to this day the work continues. In a Copenhagen museum there is a collection of Oersted's instruments (including his compass), some of his furniture, and a selection of books and pictures relating to his life.

Oersted, who was active to the end of his life, wrote many newspaper articles and founded a monthly journal of literature. In his most important nontechnical work, *The Soul of Nature,* he collected opinions on many subjects which promoted the view that the universe is a manifestation of an infinite reason and that the laws of nature are the "thoughts of God." He spoke of the cultivation of science as an exercise of religion and contended that the man of science ". . . is destined to nourish the holy frame of wisdom which shall diffuse its rays amidst the rest of mankind; it is his nightly lamp which shall enlighten the earth. Woe to him if he does not consider his vocation to be a voice from heaven."

In November 1850 Oersted's jubilee at the University of Copenhagen was celebrated by a torchlight procession of his students, past and present, to his home. At that time the Danish government presented him with a country house near Copenhagen. He did not survive to enjoy it for very long. Within a few months he became ill, and on March 9, 1851, he died peacefully.

6

ANDRÉ-MARIE AMPÈRE
1775-1836

In central France, ten kilometers north of the city of Lyon, lies the little village of Poleymieux. To a visitor, the center of interest in this quiet community is a farmhouse that occupies a lime-shaded terrace on the slopes of Mont d'Or overlooking the valley of the Saône river. The old house, now a museum, was the boyhood home of the great French scientist Ampère, who gave his name to the unit of electric current. Its ten-odd rooms are still furnished in the manner of his day and contain his books, letters, and scientific apparatus. There is a display so arranged that a visitor, by pressing buttons, can reenact the epoch-making experiments of Ampère, using his original equipment.

André-Marie Ampère was born at Lyon on January 20, 1775, into a highly respected family that had been profitably merchandising silk materials for several generations. His father, Jean-Jacques Ampère, was one of four brothers engaged in the silk business. His mother, Jeanne Sarcey, whom Jean-Jacques married at thirty-eight, was a woman of about

ANDRÉ MARIE AMPÈRE

the same age and background as her husband. At the time of their marriage the Ampère family must have been quite wealthy, for Jean-Jacques paid a rather large sum to buy the property at Poleymieux for a summer home.

For the first seven years of his life, André-Marie and his older sister, Antoinette, spent most of their time in Lyon. Their father was a cultured man who read Latin and French classics and was fascinated by Diderot and Rousseau. From his reading of Rousseau, Jean-Jacques had come to believe that the real function of a teacher was to inspire his pupils with a wish to learn rather than to instruct them in the details of any branch of knowledge. His educational ideas probably had much influence on his son's development.

Schoolmasters played only a minor part in the education of André-Marie. Like Humphry Davy, he began reading early and with almost no outside help. While still very young he also enjoyed having others read to him from such works as the famous natural-history books of Georges Buffon. He learned the names of animals and birds from the illustrations in Buffon's volumes, memorized sections dealing with natural history and important historical episodes, and learned to recite long quotations from the plays of Racine and Voltaire. As an adult he recalled how deeply he felt when, as a child of eight, he learned about the struggles between England and France over North America and the war for independence by the United States.

By the time he was fifty, Jean-Jacques Ampère had made enough money to retire from the silk business, and from 1782 he and his family regarded Poleymieux as their main home. In the quiet surroundings of this country home, André-Marie read through the twenty-eight volumes of the famous French Encyclopedia compiled by Diderot and others and first published in 1772. His long recollection of the material in the encyclopedia impressed a fellow scientist, Dominique Arago, who said of Ampère that "fifty years later he could recite long passages from the Encyclopedia on heraldry, falconry, and other subjects which had passed under his eyes in those early days." The volumes of the encyclopedia that Ampère read are still exhibited in the old bookcase where they were kept in his boyhood.

During these years André-Marie also took long country walks with his father, discussing what he had learned and observing the plants and other natural phenomena of the neighborhood. At thirteen he became interested in mathematics, probably as a result of an encyclopedia article. He devoured books on mathematics, neglecting his other studies. While he was working on algebra and conic sections he began writing a short paper on mathematics and was confronted by the strange and difficult concepts of the infinitesimal calculus. Fortunately, while he was visiting Lyon with his father, he met Professor Daburon of the Collège de la Trinité, who became his friend. During a stay at Poleymieux arranged by Ampère's father, the professor helped André-Marie with his mathematical studies and also aroused his interest in physics.

Meanwhile events in France were building up to a revolution. In 1789, when André-Marie was fourteen, the Bastille fell to an angry mob in Paris. Neither this nor any of the early incidents of the French Revolution disturbed life at Poleymieux. Along with many politically moderate people Jean-Jacques Ampère at first welcomed the revolution and even wrote a not very good play in support of the early revolutionary aim of a constitutional monarchy. However, the conduct of the Ampère family was based on monarchy and Christianity. When the Jacobins, a radical and antireligious faction, gained control of the revolutionary government, Jean-Jacques Ampère came into opposition with them and became a victim of their purges.

The circumstances of Jean-Jacques Ampère's execution were not untypical of the fate of many members of the French middle class in that period. During the time when the moderate Girondist revolutionary faction controlled the government in Lyon, Jean-Jacques Ampère served as president of the police tribunal there. In this capacity he signed the papers for the arrest of a Jacobin extremist named Chalier. A few months later the Jacobins, who had gained power in Paris, decreed that those who had opposed Chalier and his group would be brought to account for it. The Girondists in Lyon replied to this threat by executing Chalier on the guillotine that he had erected for use on others.

When Lyon later fell to the Jacobins Jean-Jacques Ampère was arrested by them. After six weeks in prison he was tried and condemned to death "as Justice of the Peace who issued the official order for the arrest of Chalier." He was executed on the guillotine on November 23, 1793.

The news was a shattering blow for the family at Poleymieux. For many months André-Marie was incapable of connected thought, and at one time his friends feared that he might never recover from the shock. However, he gradually resumed his reading, concentrating on botany, languages, and poetry. One day he was browsing through a collection of Latin poems and was struck by several lines in Horace's "Ode to Licinius":

'Tis oftener the tall pine that is shaken by the wind:
'tis the lofty towers that fall with the heavier crash,
and 'tis the tops of the mountains that the lightning strikes.

He was thrilled and turned to Latin verse with all the passion of his extraordinary nature. While wandering over the countryside on botanical excursions he declaimed to the winds and was comforted by the rhythm of the poetry. With the enthusiasm he had once given to Lagrange's profound *Mechanical Analysis*, he now recited from Homer and Virgil and wrote poems, tragedies, comedies, songs, and elegies of his own.

It was at this time that Ampère met his future wife, Julie Carron, an attractive girl from the nearby village of Saint-Germain. For her part, she was not much impressed with Ampère at first. His unprepossessing appearance, untidy dress, retiring disposition, and peculiar habit of carrying an umbrella everywhere caused her and her sister Elise to treat him as rather a joke. However, Ampère fell in love with Julie at once. His romantic attachment to her, almost as idealized as Dante's feeling for Beatrice, is recorded in a notebook made of pages torn from an old account book. Some of Ampère's entries about Julie are short diary notes, such as "Sunday 10 April 1796 I saw her for the first time" and "Her heart was embalmed with an eternal fragrance." He also wrote verses about her.

With characteristic intensity, Ampère pursued his courtship. Although he kept his love a secret for some time he found daily excuses to visit the Carron home and added such entries as the following in his journal: "I saw Julie playing aux dames after Mass" and "I found her in the garden but dared not speak." His constant presence apparently became wearing to the Carron family for at one stage they suggested that fewer visits would be welcome. In deep misery Ampère left, only to return the next morning.

If the course of his courtship was not always smooth, it was finally successful. Gradually Julie came to love him. On July 3, 1797, she and her mother visited Poleymieux and, with Madame Ampère's consent, Julie and André-Marie became engaged.

Marriage was out of the question, however, until Ampère could find a means of earning a living. Practically all of the family fortune had been confiscated, and Ampère's upbringing had scarcely prepared him for a conventional job. After he had had much discussion with friends and relatives his future brother-in-law found him a position as a private tutor of mathematics in Lyon. When Ampère was established in his new position the couple were married on August 6, 1799. At the time he was twenty-four and she was two years older.

They settled down to married life in a modest home in Lyon's Rue de Bat d'Argent. It was a friendly place for them since other members of their family lived in the town and Ampère, during his short residence there before his marriage, had developed an extensive circle of scientific and literary friends. On August 12, 1800, a son was born and they named him Jean-Jacques for Ampère's father. Like André-Marie Ampère, this second Jean-Jacques later achieved distinction as a professor at the Collège de France; he also gained renown as a friend of the famous Madame de Récamier.

Unfortunately at about this time Julie Ampère contracted an illness which was to lead to her death three years later. Beset by mounting domestic and financial worries, Ampère became more and more engrossed in his work. He bought and made apparatus to furnish a teaching laboratory and also submitted to the Lyon Academy his first scientific paper, which dealt with the identity of symmetrical polyhedrons.

Meanwhile Ampère's friends were trying to find him a better-paying teaching post more suited to his ability. Eventually he accepted an appointment in the Ecole Centrale at Bourg-en-Bresse which he planned to use as a steppingstone to a better position in Lyon. Since it was decided that his ailing wife and infant son should remain in Lyon, Ampère had to resign himself to a prolonged separation from them. Although Bourg-en-Bresse was only sixty kilometers from Lyon, the journey in those days meant a day and a half of difficult traveling that his work did not allow. The letters which passed between husband and wife during this separation are dramatic and tragic. Ampère's present a record of his fantastic energy. He rose at an early hour to prepare his lectures for the day and filled every available moment with chemical experiments and the writing of his memoirs. He tells of accidents in his laboratory which ruined his clothes and burned his beard. On one occasion he narrowly escaped the loss of an eye. Julie's letters are more pathetic. They describe the anxiety of a concerned but helpless mother and present the picture of a child with frayed sleeves, stained pants, and garments covered with multicolored patches.

Ampère was able to return to spend only the last weeks with his wife, who died on July 13, 1803. His reaction to her death is recorded as a Latin dialogue between God and a faithful person regarding the trials of man and God's ultimate mercy. At the end of the dialogue God says, "I will fasten my eyes upon you and will instruct you in the path along which you will go." The entry about his wife's death is the last in Ampère's journal.

In his frantic efforts to secure a teaching post in Lyon, Ampère came to realize that he should provide concrete evidence of his qualifications as a mathematician. For years he had been mulling over a problem connected with the calculus of probability, and he decided that his ideas were a good subject for a paper. His thinking was far in advance of the time, but it impressed Joseph de Lalande, a celebrated astronomer who was then in Bourg. Lalande called the paper to the notice of two government commissioners who were visiting different educational establishments for the purpose of recruiting a staff for the lycée at Lyon, then widely considered the most outstanding residential college in France. As a result Ampère received an appointment as professor of mathematics at the lycée and left Bourg on April 17, 1803.

Ampère kept his Lyon appointment less than twelve months. The loss of Julie just when he had found a means to return to her completely unsettled him. For a second time in his life his mental state caused great concern to his family and friends. He began to talk of going to Paris and announced that he would go into business selling chemical products. The letters his mother wrote to him from Poleymieux during this crisis reveal a great strength of character and understanding. With her support he was diverted from his business schemes and his scientific friends helped him to secure an appointment in Paris as assistant professor at the Ecole Polytechnique.

Soon after Ampère had taken up residence in Paris a friend introduced him to the Potot family. At the age of thirty-one he married the Potot daughter, then aged twenty-six. The match was not a happy one. Ampère and his new wife lived with her parents, whose materialistic outlook and other values were the complete antithesis of his own upbringing. While he lived in the household his distinguished visitors were insulted and he was relegated to an attic. When his wife became pregnant she and her parents were so bitter in their behavior toward him that he finally moved to lodgings provided for him by the Minister of the Interior. After the separation his daughter Albine was born on July 6, 1807. Later this daughter was to add to the tragedies of the family by marrying an army officer who was an alcoholic and frequently under arrest.

Left in a very depressed state of mind by his misfortunes, Ampère turned to metaphysics for comfort. However, he did not permit his interest in religious philosophy to interfere with his professional and scientific activities. In 1809, while he was teaching at the Ecole Polytechnique and writing abstruse papers on mathematics, he was also appointed Inspector General of the university. The new position took him away from Paris for weeks at a time and involved inspecting schools in the provinces and reporting on the quality of the teachers. Besides such official duties he found time for research in chemistry and mathematics and also contributed an article to the *Annales de Chimie et de Physique* (Annals of Chemistry and Physics) in which he supported Humphry Davy's opposition to the phlogiston theory of combustion. As a result of the article the two scientists began a three-year correspondence, and they met and talked when Davy visited Paris at the end of 1813.

Although at this time he had to adjust to the death of his mother and to that of Elise, Julie's sister, with whom he had been close, he seemed more prepared to cope with these shocks. His life changed for the better in other ways too. In 1814 he was awarded the Cross of the French Legion of Honor, and during the next two years, learned societies everywhere competed to honor him. By this time he also had reason to be proud of the progress of his son Jean-Jacques, who did so well in his studies that he received a Prix d'Honneur on completing his course in philosophy. Besides all this, Ampère became more settled in his home life. For himself and his sister Josephine he purchased a small house and garden at No. 19 Fosses-Saint-Victor near the Jardin des Plantes. The family home at Poleymieux was sold to meet the cost.

Ampère was now enjoying his dual employment, teaching at the Polytechnique and inspecting schools of the university, any spare time being fully occupied with developments in mathematics, philosophy, and chemistry, when suddenly he produced such a brilliant explosion of original ideas as to establish him as one of the greatest contributors to electrical science. It was in his comprehensive study of electrodynamics that above all his other discoveries he made his name.

The appearance of Oersted's famous pamphlet on electromagnetism in 1820 marked a turning point in Ampère's career. On September 4, 1820, the French physicist Dominique Arago made a report on the paper at a meeting of the French Institute in Paris which Ampère attended. Of all the scientists who were excited by the new scientific breakthrough—including Arago, Biot, Davy, Faraday, Henry, and Berzelius—Ampère was the most energetic and best equipped mathematically to solve the problems raised by

Oersted. Arago's report started Ampère on a train of thought that absorbed his complete attention. Within fourteen days he had constructed apparatus, carried out experiments, recorded the results, and translated his findings into mathematical formulas. On September 18 he submitted his first paper on electromagnetism to the Academy. In it he showed how the Oersted effect depended on the relative position of the wire and the needle. To explain how the effect worked, he invented his "bon Homme d'Ampère," a hypothetical little man who always swam in the same direction as the current and always faced toward the magnetic needle. When "bon Homme d'Ampère" swam face downward above the needle the north pole moved to his left. When he swam on his back below the needle it still moved to his left. Thus he developed the idea of magnetic force arising from the circular action of current around the electric wire. This rule, with its later modifications, is used today in practical design work.

Ampère found that by twisting the wire into a spiral around the needle he could produce a stronger effect than with a straight wire. He also observed that the reaction of the needle increased with the number of turns in the spiral. In this way he anticipated the instrument for measuring current devised by Schweigger a few months later and known as a "multiplier." Ampère gave this device the name of "galvanometer." We are also indebted to him for the word "electrodynamic," a term that he used to classify all the phenomena he observed when he brought together two current-carrying wires. For example, two wires carrying current in the same direction attracted one another, but when the currents were in opposite directions repulsion took place—a major discovery that caused widespread interest and scientific speculation. But Ampère was always ahead in his new ideas, and at meeting after meeting of the Académie he increased the store of knowledge. At times he astonished the illustrious members, as for instance when, instead of using a magnetized compass needle to point to the north, he delicately suspended a helix of wire, the ends of which dipped into mercury-cup contacts to carry the currents in and out, and thus showed that even without an iron bar the same effect was produced by a copper wire carrying current.

Within a few days after seeing Arago's demonstration Ampère had conceived the idea of sending messages by means of the electric current and receiving them by the electromagnetic effect—the principle involved in the electric telegraph. He also developed the electromagnet, in which an iron rod was placed within the hollow center formed by a long coil of wire. When the current was on, the iron rod became magnetized so that it would attract and hold other pieces of iron until the current was shut off. This piece of equipment has had many practical applications in electrical engineering. Another of Ampère's inventions was the astatic needle, which consists of two similar magnetic needles pointing in opposite directions and suspended as one unit. The needles are fixed rigidly to one another so that they remain one above the other and a short distance apart. In this device the controlling influence of the earth's magnetic field is reduced and the needle can therefore respond more sensitively to other magnetic forces.

For several years Ampère continued to make important contributions in the field of electromagnetism. In electrical history the significance of his discoveries and analysis was equaled only by Faraday's work a decade later. It was Ampère who developed an electrical explanation of magnetism in iron and explained the origin of the earth's magnetic state. His comprehensive mathematical treatment of electromagnetic phenomena led to the formulas based on the integral calculus that constitute the very essence of present-day electromagnetic theory. Of his work Arago said that "the vast field of physical science perhaps never presented so brilliant a discovery, conceived, verified, and completed with such rapidity."

Ampère's studies in electrodynamics, begun when he was forty-five, brought him to the peak of his career and fame. They also imposed a heavy strain on his health, already undermined by several breakdowns caused by the succession of personal tragedies and professional disappointments in his life. In 1829 he had a serious attack of pneumonia. He never completely recovered from its effects and aged rapidly from that time on. He spent the few remaining years of his life in Lyon and the south, and died at Marseilles on June 11, 1836, at the age of sixty-one.

Forty years earlier Ampère's father, awaiting his execution at the scaffold, had written a moving letter ending with the words "as to my son there is nothing that I do not expect of him." History has shown that few men have lived more deeply, more honestly, or to greater purpose than that son who so completely justified a father's ambition.

7

MICHAEL FARADAY

1791-1867

Until Oersted's time, magnetism and electricity had been explored as separate and distinct forces with no more than a suspicion that they were connected in some way. Oersted's discovery of the effect of current on a magnetic needle, reinforced by Ampère's experiments and analysis, provided the first advance toward the integration of these two sets of phenomena. Like many important breakthroughs, the discovery that electricity could be converted into magnetism raised at least as many questions as it answered. One of the most intriguing was the possibility of producing an opposite effect, that is, of converting magnetism into electricity. Ampère's electromagnet offered a partial answer to this question, but it was Michael Faraday who carried the problem through to a complete solution.

In developing the processes that converted magnetism into electricity, Faraday devised the first electric transformer and the first generator. He was also the first scientist to suggest that the important element in electromagnetic phenomena was not electric or magnetic particles but the space in which they operated. Thus he originated the

MICHAEL FARADAY

idea of the force field, a concept that is basic to modern electromagnetic theory.

Michael Faraday was born on September 22, 1791, in Newington Butts, South London, England. His father James was a blacksmith who had brought his wife to London from Clapham Village, on the borders of Yorkshire and Lancashire, after their marriage. In their earlier home both parents had been members of a small religious sect known as the Sandemanians, and Faraday inherited their religious faith. His lifelong adherence to this faith and his deep religious convictions outlived the founder who died at Danbury, Connecticut, twenty years before Faraday was born.

According to Faraday's diary, his formal schooling did not amount to much more that "the rudiments of reading, writing and arithmetic in a common day school." At the age of thirteen he was hired as an errand boy by a Mr. Ribeau who had a bookshop on Blandford Street in the West End of London. In those days it was the practice of news agents to rent out their newspapers. Subscribers were allowed to keep the paper for a limited time and then the copy was carried to the next reader. It was young Faraday's responsibility to handle such arrangements and he carried out the duties so efficiently that his employer was impressed. About a year after he had started to work he was formally apprenticed to learn the trade of bookbinding under Mr. Ribeau, who waived the usual apprentice's fee "in consideration of . . . [Faraday's] . . . faithful services. . . ."

During the seven years of his apprenticeship Faraday used his time and opportunities not only to learn the trade but to read the books in Mr. Ribeau's shop. One work that he singled out later as having had a great influence on his life was the 1809 edition of Dr. Isaac Watts's *On the Mind*. Faraday considered his reading of it as the starting point of his intellectual development.

Among the books in Mr. Ribeau's shop he also found scientific writings that caught his imagination. He was entranced by Jane Marcet's *Conversations in Chemistry* and began performing experiments to test the facts that she presented. Mrs. Marcet, who was the wife of a Swiss physician living in London, later became his friend. Another work which fed his early interest in science appeared in the second edition of the *Encyclopaedia Britannica* published in Edinburgh in 1797. Its fifty pages contained a significant and comprehensive summary of the knowledge of electricity at the time. Along with *Conversations in Chemistry,* he mentions this article as particularly helpful to him. Of the two, Mrs. Marcet's work had a greater influence on the young apprentice; his electrical interests did not prevail over chemistry until a later time.

In addition to his voracious reading, Faraday carried out scientific experiments and attended public lectures on scientific subjects whenever possible. One day while walking along Fleet Street he noticed an announcment of a course of lectures on natural philosophy to be given by a Mr. Tatum. At one shilling a lecture, the price would have been beyond his means if he had not received help from his older brother Robert, who carried on with the blacksmith business of their father after his death in 1810.

Faraday got a great deal of information for his money, judging from his notes on the lectures. Now on exhibit at the Royal Institution, they are written in a clear and beautiful script and occupy four volumes bound in leather by Faraday himself. They are illustrated with his own sketches and are dedicated to Mr. Ribeau as a way of thanking his employer for encouraging his studies and offering him the use of his books.

Along with the notes, Faraday added comments of his own. In one volume he describes how he was able to cover the lectures in such great detail, and the account is interesting as a revelation of his painstaking personality. He wrote: "My method was to take with me a sheet or two of paper stitched or pinned up the middle so as to form something like a book—I usually get a front seat and then, placing my hat on my knees and my paper on the hat I . . . set down the most prominent words, short but important sentences, titles of the experiments, names of what substances came under consideration and many other hints that would tend to bring what had passed to my mind. On leaving the lecture room I proceeded immediately homewards and, on that and the next night, had generally drawn up a second set of notes. . . . These were to be my guide whilst writing out the lectures in a rough manner. . . . I then referred to memory for the matter belonging to each subject and I believe that I have not let much of the meaning and sense of Mr. Tatum's lectures slip."

Another of Faraday's writing projects begun at this time was his Common Place Book, which is now in the library of the Institution of Electrical Engineers in London. In it he collected ideas, quotations, stories, poems, experimental results, and other items that caught his interest, including an account about an American boy with extraordinary powers of mental calculation and a "Receipt to make Gin." One of his statements, "Bodies do not act where they are not," indicates that the young apprentice was already considering the idea of action at a distance which became an important feature in his later analysis of lines of force. Faraday, who had gotten the notion of keeping such a record from the philosopher John Locke, also indexed the entries according to a system that Locke himself had used. Without such care it is hard to see how he could have located anything in the book, since it eventually ran to over four hundred pages.

A few months before the completion of his apprenticeship, Faraday attracted the interest of a customer at Mr. Ribeau's shop, a member of the Royal Institution. This man, named Mr. Dance, took Faraday to hear a course of lectures by Sir Humphry Davy. Occupying a seat in the gallery that is still pointed out to visitors, the twenty-year-old apprentice looked down, fascinated both by the glittering, fashionable audience and by the brilliantly lit lecture table on which novel apparatus was displayed and original experiments carried out. He took copious notes, which later he wrote up, bound in leather and sent to Davy with a letter applying for a post at the Royal Institution.

Meanwhile Faraday had completed his apprenticeship and reluctantly engaged himself as a journeyman bookbinder to a new employer. He had been with his new job only a few months when the dismissal of an unsatisfactory assistant created a vacancy at the Royal Institution. On Christmas Eve 1812 a carriage and pair pulled up to the door of the modest household on Weymouth Street where Faraday lived. A footman descended, knocked loudly, and handed in a letter for Mr. Faraday. It was from Sir Humphry Davy, who wrote that he was going out of town but wished to see Faraday on his return. The following March, Faraday was appointed as Davy's assistant. His wages were twenty-five shillings a week and he was provided with two rooms as living quarters at the Royal Institution.

After a few months of the bottle-washing kind of jobs in the Institution laboratory, Faraday was offered an exciting and unexpected opportunity. Sir Humphry and Lady Davy were planning to spend a year and a half abroad on a Grand Tour of Europe. Faraday was invited to join the party to perform secretarial work and assist Davy in carrying out a program of scientific research. Unfortunately for Faraday, Davy's personal valet withdrew from the tour at the last moment and the young man found himself performing in the servant's place. These unexpected duties, along with Lady Davy's overbearing attitude toward him, marred some of his enjoyment of the trip. Nonetheless, it was an impressive experience for him. He was able to visit France, Italy, and Switzerland and, as the traveling companion of a noted scientist, he met many of the famous men of the day.

The tour began at a time when England, France, and other European countries were fighting the campaigns of the Napoleonic wars. On October 19, 1813, a few days before Davy's departure for Paris, Napoleon had been forced back at the Battle of Leipzig, and in other parts of Europe the armies of England, Prussia, and Austria were assembling to give battle to the French. Yet in spite of the atmosphere of war, Davy's party set off in a horse-drawn carriage from Albemarle Street in London bound for Plymouth, where they were to cross the channel to France. They took with them a large amount of baggage, including two boxes of laboratory equipment, and Faraday's diary mentions problems with customs officials during the journey. He also reported that when the party crossed the Alps a gang of fifty men had to be employed to carry everything on sleds over the high passes. To get the Davy carriage across the channel and over the mountains the wheels were removed and carried separately.

After their channel crossing from England, the party landed at Morlaix, France. Davy, because of his international reputation, was able to obtain French passports, which helped them in dealing with local authorities. The party also received special privileges of admission to museums, libraries, and other public institutions "not only on the usual opening days but on any day." During their journey through France they were sometimes in close contact with military operations, but rarely was the tour seriously interrupted.

When the party arrived in Paris some of the scientists who visited Davy brought samples of a recently discovered substance and asked his opinion of it. Using their traveling laboratory, Davy's party spent several days carrying out tests on the new material, iodine.

During his stay in Paris, Faraday met Ampère. While attending a lecture by Joseph Gay-Lussac at the Ecole Polytechnique he became interested in a very large voltaic battery that had been developed at government expense. One of his memorable nonscientific experiences was his view of Napoleon, whom he described as "sitting in the corner of his carriage almost hidden from sight by an enormous robe of ermine, his face overshadowed by a tremendous plume of feathers that descended from a velvet hat. His carriage was very rich and fourteen servants stood upon it at various parts." Commenting on the reaction of the French people to the sight of Napoleon he said that "no acclamation was heard where I stood and no comments."

On leaving Paris the party traveled southward through Nemours, Moulins, Montpellier, and Nice. In the course of the journey various scientific tests were made for the purpose of detecting the presence of the newly discovered iodine in various plants. From Nice the party turned north into the Alps, where Faraday made barometric readings as they went along. Two weeks in Florence seem to have been crowded with museum visits to see Galileo's first telescope, an abundance of electrical apparatus, and an unusual collection of magnets. The climax of this sightseeing was an "extremely beautiful and interesting" demonstration during which several diamonds were vaporized in an oxygen-filled glass globe using the great burning glass of the Grand Duke of Tuscany. While in Italy Faraday also saw and studied the live crater of the volcano Vesuvius and met Alessandro Volta, whom he described as "a hale elderly man, very free in conversation."

The party returned to London at the end of April 1815. A few days later Faraday was reappointed at the Royal Institution. He was given a more responsible position, as assistant in the laboratory and superintendent of the apparatus, and a raise in salary to thirty shillings a week.

During the next few years Faraday began to earn a reputation as a chemist. His first published paper, an analysis of some caustic lime from Tuscany, appeared in 1816 in the *Quarterly Journal of Science* issued by the Royal Institution. In 1820 a paper of his on several new chemical compounds was read before the Royal Society of London and became the first of his articles to appear in the Society's *Philosophical Transactions*.

When Oersted and Ampère announced their discoveries regarding electromagnetism in 1820, the subject caught the imagination of many scientists, including Sir Humphry Davy. Faraday, partly led by Davy's interest, also began to turn his attention to electrical phenomena. While he continued to work in chemistry he also built up a background of electrical knowledge by reading, writing, lecturing, and experimenting. In 1821 he wrote a significant paper, "History of the Progress of Electromagnetism," and then began to investigate the possibilities of producing rotation by magnetic means. While others were experimenting with the use of current to cause rotation of a magnet on its axis, he decided that the current could produce rotation, not of the magnet itself, but of its magnetic poles around the conducting wire.

In his diary he described his first successful trial of this idea. According to his account he "arranged a magnet needle in a glass tube with mercury about it and by a cork, water, etc., supported a connecting wire so that its upper end should go into the silver cup and its mercury and the lower end move in the channel of mercury round the pole of the magnet. Very satisfactory but make more sensible apparatus."

Within a few weeks he had made his more sensible apparatus. It was an arrangement which did away with the magnet and caused the current-carrying wire to rotate by the influence of the earth's magnetic field. On Christmas Day 1823 his brother-in-law, George Barnard, witnessed the experiment. Observing Faraday's reaction as the small wire began to revolve, he wrote: "I shall never forget the enthusiasm expressed in his face and the sparkling in his eyes."

Faraday's friend and biographer, John Tyndall, said that Mrs. Farady was also present during this experiment. At the time, she had been married to Faraday for eighteen months. Her maiden name was Sarah Barnard and she was the daughter of an elder of the Sandemanian Church who worked as a silversmith in Paternoster Row by St. Paul's Cathedral. Judging from the references to her in Faraday's diary and the letters he wrote to her, they were devoted to one another. She seems to have been content with her life at the Royal Institution and did not resent his dedication to his scientific career.

For Faraday, the years of the 1820's were a period of preparation for his climactic discoveries in the early 1830's. Throughout the decade his own developing ideas were being enriched and stimulated by the work of others who were exploring electromagnetism. An important observation in the field was made by the French professor of physics Dominique Arago, who noticed that the oscillations of a pivoted magnetic needle became sluggish when it was brought near a sheet of copper. Arago also discovered that a disc of metal, when rotated, would drag a nearby magnetic needle around with it although there appeared to be no connection between the two.

In the early 1820's a German, Johann Salomo Christoph Schweigger of Halle, repeated Oersted's experiment and found that the reaction of the needle could be doubled if the current-carrying wire itself were doubled so that it passed back under the needle. He reported that the effect on the needle increased in direct relationship to the number of times the wire made the double turn over and under the needle. In 1825 a cobbler-scientist in Woolwich, England, named William Sturgeon, produced the first electromagnet for practical use as distinct from Ampère's laboratory apparatus. It consisted of a piece of stout iron wire bent into the form of a horseshoe. The wire, coated with insulating varnish, was bound round with sixteen bare copper wires, the turns being separated from one another. When the current from a single voltaic pair of 130-square-inch plates in acid was passed through the winding, the magnet held a weight of nine pounds—a wonderful performance in those days.

Faraday was following all these developments with great interest and also benefited from Davy's interest in electromagnetism. Two curious effects that Davy called to Faraday's attention were the fact that a copper wire carrying a current would pick up iron filings and that a wire carrying a current would be attracted or repelled by a magnet.

Considering all these phenomena, Faraday became more and more fascinated by the possibility of producing an electric current from a magnet. By 1831 the problem had become such a preoccupation that he gave up a time-consuming research project on optical glass to concentrate on electrical research. A few months later he had carried to complete success his two most outstanding experiments. The date of his first breakthrough in solving the problem of converting magnetism into electricity was August 29, 1831. On that day he took a soft iron ring seven-eights of an inch thick and 6 inches in its external diameter. Around one half of the ring's circumference (which he called Side A) he wound three coils of wire. Each winding had 24 feet of wire and the turns in the windings were separated by twine and calico. Leaving a separating space between the two sides of the ring he wound the other half (called Side B) with 60 feet of wire in two separate coils. This original ring, the

COURTESY BURNDY LIBRARY

Forerunner of the modern generator, Faraday's dynamo was the first machine that could convert mechanical energy into electrical energy by electromagnetic means.

forerunner of the modern electrical transformer, is now among the famous exhibits of the Royal Institution.

Having prepared the ring, Faraday proceeded to connect the two coils on the B side in series and carried the connecting wire over a magnetic needle. Then he connected one of the A side coils to a battery. When he closed the battery circuit on the A side the magnetic needle on the B side was deflected, oscillated, and quickly settled back in its original position. Faraday observed no further effect on the needle until he broke the battery connection. Then, to his astonishment, there was another kick of the needle, this time in the opposite direction.

The absence of a permanent current in the secondary—to use modern transformer terminology—while the current in the primary was still flowing disappointed him, but he felt he was on the right track. For weeks he tried every possible variation in the assembly of his apparatus. Eventually he replaced the wound-iron ring by a "hollow helix" or solenoid. It was a cylinder formed by the windings of eight lengths of copper wire each of which was 27½ feet long. All the eight windings were connected in parallel (that is, separately, and not in a series) to a galvanometer. He then thrust a cylindrical bar magnet into the solenoid and produced an immediate deflection of the galvanometer. While he left the magnet in the solenoid the needle fell back to zero, but when he withdrew it the action of withdrawal produced a second deflection, this time in the opposite direction. The experiments made on October 17, 1831, proved that current resulted from the relative motion of a conductor and magnetic field. The device he had assembled was the ancestor of the modern electric generator.

After this discovery the production of a steady current followed as a logical development but only after intense thought and frustrating experiment. To produce the necessary motion involved in generating a current, Faraday arranged a copper disc on a brass axle for turning. Wires, in rubbing contact with the edge of the disc and the axle, were connected to a galvanometer, and the disc was placed so that its outer edge rotated between the two poles of a horseshoe magnet. First experiments were a failure but when the disc was rotated between the poles of a powerful magnet made available by the Royal Society, the galvanometer needle showed continuous deflection. The experiment was a complete success: the first direct-current dynamo. On November 24, 1831, three weeks after the dynamo experiment, Faraday reported his work in a paper which he read before the Royal Society. His presentation was an epoch-making event.

During this remarkable series of experimental discoveries, Faraday had given much thought to possible explanations of the underlying principles. What really was the connection between electricity and magnetism?

He was above all a practical scientist and not a theoretical mathematician, but what emerged from the thinking was a stroke of genius. He formulated the idea of lines of force in the space between those bodies which showed electrical and magnetic properties. As he studied the pattern assumed by iron filings sprinkled over a card laid on a magnet or on a wire carrying a current he gradually developed the conception of a field of force associated with these curved lines. This not only gave Faraday an explanation of the experimental results he had produced, but ultimately proved to be the starting point for electromagnetic theory which today has spread through the entire study of electricity. It was probably the greatest of all his contributions.

In 1853 Faraday was appointed Superintendent of the House at the Royal Institution and Director of the Laboratory. His salary, which had been fixed at £200 a year for the previous forty years was increased to £300 a year. Five years after this appointment he took up residence in a house on Hampton Court Green near London presented to him by Queen Victoria. By this time he had begun to have fits of giddiness and loss of memory, and in 1865 he retired. He died on August 25, 1867. At his own request, he was buried without pomp or ceremony in a simple grave at Highgate Cemetery, London.

JOSEPH HENRY

8

JOSEPH HENRY
1797-1878

In the history of electrical development Faraday's discoveries have thrown an undeserved shadow over the achievements of Joseph Henry. Independently of each other, both men discovered electromagnetic induction—the process by which magnetism could be converted into electricity. Although Henry's work seems to have been earlier, Faraday was the first to publish the revolutionary finding and fairly won the lion's share of credit. Yet for his own independent discovery of the process and all his other contributions to electrical development, Henry earned a prominent place among the giants of electrical science.

His accomplishments were the more impressive because he was so far away from Europe, where scientific progress was concentrated at that time. While scientists on the other side of the Atlantic were close enough to each other to exchange information on developments and experiments within days after they occurred, Henry was dependent on scientific news gleaned from casual travelers to Europe and from the few scientific journals that arrived several months after their publication. Since there were then few scientists in the United States, he was deprived of the mental stimulation of discussion with others in his field. Besides these disadvantages, he lacked the funds and laboratory facilities which were provided in the European centers of science and learning. His references to his difficulties in obtaining the simple necessities for carrying out experiments when his brain was teeming with ideas makes sad reading: "Not a piece of zinc to be found in the whole town," "Iron bonnet-wire available but not as good as copper and very expensive," "Must wait until August when the room will be available and the students will not take all my time."

In spite of these obstacles he made many fundamental electrical discoveries. His name, Henry, is now universally used for an important fundamental electrical unit. His fame rests also on the founding and directing of the Smithsonian Institution.

Joseph Henry was born in Albany, New York. The date of his birth is not certain, but the evidence seems to indicate that it was December 9, 1797, although there are claims for a date two years later. His parents, William Henry (originally Hendrie) and Ann Alexander, were both born in Scotland. As children they had been brought to America by their families on the same ship and had arrived in New York on June 17, 1775, the day of the Battle of Bunker Hill. On their arrival in America the Hendrie and Alexander families separated. However, they met again after the American Revolution and William and Ann were eventually married. Joseph's mother was a devout member of the Scottish Presbyterian Church, and has been described as fair, with classic features and personal charm. Little is known about his father except that he was modestly employed and changed the family name from Hendrie to Henry to his son's later regret. Because of his parents' poor health, when he was still a very young child Joseph was sent to live with his maternal grandmother in the small town of Galway, north of Albany. There he attended the village school and, at the age of ten, took a part-time job in the village store.

During this time of his life, Joseph Henry was not particularly studious. He had a lively nature which made him popular in the store and with the boys in the village, but he also liked to daydream, a tendency he never entirely lost. According to a story he later told about himself he seems to have had difficulty making up his mind when faced with several choices of action. The village shoemaker had been instructed to make him a pair of shoes to his own liking. When the shoemaker asked Henry whether he wanted square toes or round ones, the boy could not decide. Time and time again when the shoemaker pressed him to make up his mind, Henry put him off by telling him to go ahead with the rest of the shoe. One day when Henry arrived for his usual discussion about the shoes he was presented with a completed pair. One shoe had a round toe and the other a square one.

Henry did not become interested in books until he was thirteen. One day as he was chasing a tame rabbit that had escaped under the raised floor of the village church, he noticed some loose boards which gave him entrance to the inside. For the first time in his life, he found himself before shelves of books. Becoming interested in a rather sober book, *The Fool of Quality,* by Sir Philip Brooks, he forgot the rabbit and began browsing through its pages. Day after day he returned through the hole in the floor to his newly found world of books. Mr. Broderick, his employer, was the first to discover what Henry was doing. A great reader himself, he was sympathetic and arranged matters so that Henry could enter the library through the door.

After his father's death Joseph Henry returned to his mother's home in Albany and was apprenticed to a watchmaker. He showed no particular aptitude for the trade although he probably learned many of the techniques which later enabled him to make apparatus for his scientific experiments. When Henry had finished only two years of his apprenticeship his employer had to give up his business. Henry, who was then sixteen, did not find a steady job although his mother had to let rooms to keep her home together. Instead he began to spend his time at the local theater where he made himself useful by helping behind the scenes. Soon afterward he organized an amateur dramatic society himself and began acting in and writing plays.

Henry was lured away from his theatrical interests after one of his mother's boarders lent him a copy of *Lectures on Experimental Philosophy,* by a Rev. G. Gregory, rector of a church near London. The author's method was to ask simple questions such as "Why should not the flame of a candle drop towards the floor, when you hold it downwards instead of ascending into the air? . . . You look into a well of water and see your own face and figure as if painted there: why is this? You are told that it is done by reflection of light. But what is reflection of light?" Henry's copy of the book, preserved in his library, has the following note on the flyleaf in his own handwriting:

"This book, although by no means a profound work, has, under Providence, exerted a remarkable influence upon my life. It accidentally fell into my hands when I was about sixteen years old, and was the first book I ever read with attention. It opened to me a new world of thought and enjoyment; invested things before almost unnoticed with the highest interest; fixed my mind on the study of nature, and caused me to resolve at the time of reading it, that I would immediately commence to devote my life to the acquisition of knowledge. J. H."

To follow up his new interest, Henry began to attend night classes in geometry and mechanics at the Albany Academy and studied English grammar under a private instructor. To help meet family expenses he took a position as teacher in a district school. In his two occupations as student and teacher he spent some sixteen hours a day in the classroom. In spite of this heavy schedule he passed his entrance examinations for the academy with honors less than a year after he had begun his studies.

After he had attended the academy for a while Henry was given the job of helping Dr. Beck, the principal there, to set up the experimental apparatus he was using for public lectures. It was while doing this work that he developed the practice of repeating experiments he had heard about and testing the results himself.

On the recommendation of Dr. Beck, Henry eventually secured a position as private tutor in the family of Stephen Van Rensselaer the founder of what is now Rensselaer Polytechnic Institute at Troy, New York. During the two years with the Van Rensselaer family he had many leisure hours during which he furthered his scientific education.

In 1824 two scientific societies in Albany merged to form the Albany Institute. Henry, who had taken an interest in the societies while working for Dr. Beck, was appointed the institute's librarian. In the fall of that year he was persuaded to deliver his first public lecture, "On the Chemical and Mechanical Effects of Steam." His presentation, accompanied by experimental demonstrations, was a great success. The following spring he gave another talk, entitled "The Production of Cold by the Rarefaction of Air," and he introduced some experiments of spectacular appeal to his audience.

While he was at the institute, Henry's health began to show the effects of his hard-driving years of study and work. Taking the advice of family and friends, he accepted an appointment which allowed him to work outdoors, becoming a surveyor on a road-building project between West Point and Lake Erie. When the job was finished in 1826 Henry was offered a number of positions. Some of them would have permitted him to continue his outdoor life and one was an invitation from Dr. Beck to occupy the chair of mathematics at the Albany Academy. Henry, who had enjoyed his outside work, hesitated for a time before making up his mind. Finally he accepted the academy position although it meant working inside and paid less than other jobs he might have taken. He received his appointment in April 1826 and took up his duties in the fall of that year.

It was at this point in his career that Henry began to take a serious interest in electromagnetism. In 1825 William Sturgeon in England had exhibited examples of his electromagnet before the Society of Arts in London. The invention reached New York a year later.

Henry, after observing its construction and operation, decided to make one like it. Since the United States was not as well supplied as Europe with the material for scientific experiments, he ran into some difficulty in obtaining the things he needed: a bar of soft iron for the core, a length of copper wire to make the windings around the core, and, hardest of all, a voltaic battery of sufficient size to produce the proper amount of current in the wire. Somehow he managed to overcome these problems, and, in producing his own electromagnet, he introduced new features to increase the strength of the device.

While Sturgeon had used a bare copper wire for his windings and spaced out the turns so that they never touched each other, Henry insulated the wire so that the turns could be wound closely together around the iron bar. Because of the insulation Henry was also able to supply more than one layer of wire on his magnet. His first layered coil was exhibited at the Albany Academy in June 1828. Another of his electromagnets, insulated with strips of silk ribbon cut from his wife's silk petticoat, is preserved at the Princeton Museum. In one of his electromagnets he wound over 35 feet of silk-covered wire in layers that made over four hundred turns around the iron core, and he found he could get a lifting power much greater than the 9 pounds raised by Sturgeon's invention. To produce the stronger effects he used various sizes and arrangements of plates in his battery and different coils of wire. For one of his electromagnets he wound nine separate wires around the iron core and connected them in parallel (that is, separately) to the same battery, which consisted of less than half a square foot of zinc. With this magnet he found that he could raise the lifting power to 750 pounds in a step-by-step process as he connected more and more of the nine coils to the battery.

In experimenting with variations of electromagnets, Henry learned a great deal about the behavior of electric circuits, and some of his findings anticipated the work of

Georg Ohm, discussed in the next chapter. He noticed that a magnet which would lift only a few pounds with one type of battery connection might lift many more pounds with another type. The idea of relating the battery to the winding grew in his mind, and his use of the terms "intensity" and "quantity" was his way of distinguishing between the electrical effects produced by using a single long coil with a battery of many plates in series and by using a number of short multiple coils connected to a single battery. The different effects are now better understood and identified as voltage (intensity effect) and current (quantity effect).

The idea of defining magnetic force as a ratio of lifting power to weight of magnet developed from these experiments. In one magnet he achieved a figure of 420 for the ratio. He compared this result with the magnet which had been worn by Sir Isaac Newton in a ring. Newton's magnet weighed only a few grains and would lift a piece of iron 250 times its own weight.

Henry published a report on the results of his work to increase the strength of electromagnets in the *American Journal of Science* for January 1831. It was his first article in a recognized scientific publication. The report was added as an appendix to the *Journal* with a statement by Henry that he was publishing his results because he had learned of similar work by a Professor Moll of Utrecht in The Netherlands. The editors of the *Journal* had added a comment that "this article appeared too late for insertion in its proper place: its importance induces us to give it in an appendix." Moll's article, which appeared in the same issue, concerned a magnet that would lift between 150 and 200 pounds.

The experience of finding that others were working on

the same problems as he and publishing their results before he did might have been a lesson to Henry on the folly of deferring publication of his discoveries. Yet even after this incident he delayed publishing his discovery of electromagnetic induction until after Faraday had reported the same discovery.

Not too long before the publication of his first article, Henry had married. His wife was his first cousin, Harriet, the daughter of a widowed aunt who had been living in Schenectady. Henry had been visiting his cousin in Schenectady and married her in 1830 shortly after she, her mother, and her brother had moved to Albany. They seem to have had quite a happy marriage although very little is recorded about their life together. Of the children born to them, three daughters and one son survived beyond babyhood, but the son died in 1862.

COURTESY BURNDY LIBRARY

As part of his work on improving electromagnets, Henry constructed one that supported more than a ton of iron.

While he had been experimenting to increase the power of electromagnets Henry had, like Faraday, discovered electromagnetic induction. Although his discovery probably came earlier than Faraday's, he did not publish his finding until shortly after he had read about Faraday's work. Henry's report, which appeared in the July 1832 issue of the *American Journal of Science,* quoted from an announcement on Faraday's experiments that appeared in the published proceedings of the Royal Institution dated February 17, 1832. Henry then went on to say that "before having any knowledge of the method given in the above account I had succeeded in producing electrical effects in the following manner . . . a piece of copper wire about thirty feet long and covered with elastic varnish was closely coiled around the middle of the soft iron armature of the galvanic magnet described in volume 19 of the *American Journal of Science* which, when excited, will sustain six hundred and seventy pounds. The winding of the magnet core ends in mercury cups connected to distant galvanometer by wire forty feet long.

"Galvanic battery attached to magnet suddenly immersed in dilute acid. At instant of immersion N. end of needle deflected 30° to W. Therefore, current from the helix. Only a single impulse. The needle after a few oscillations resumed its former undisturbed position in magnetic meridian although the galvanic action of the battery and consequently the magnetic power still continued. When battery was withdrawn, needle suddenly deflected 20° to E. Operation repeated many times.

"This experiment illustrates most strikingly the reciprocal action of the two principles of electricity and magnetism if indeed it does not establish their absolute identity. . . . We have thus as it were electricity converted into magnetism and this magnetism again into electricity."

Henry also reported another observation he had made during this experiment. After the battery had been disconnected from the magnet and the needle had come to rest, the armature had been pulled away from the magnet to which it had remained attached by magnetism that still remained in the iron core. Immediately a current was observed on the galvanometer. By moving the armature small steps at a time

Henry experimented with this apparatus and discovered self-induction, or the phenomenon of an "extra current," which opposed the dying out of current.

the galvanometer needle also moved in small steps, all in the same direction. "From the foregoing facts," Henry wrote, "it appears that a current of electricity is produced, for an instant, in a helix of copper surrounding a soft piece of iron whenever magnetism is induced in the iron."

In further experiments he arranged in various ways an iron link between a battery coil and a coil connected to a galvanometer and showed the same mutual induction between the two coils. Henry's report of these experiments is accepted as evidence that he discovered, independently, the principle of the mutual induction ring which Faraday also developed.

In his article Henry disclosed at least one discovery that he was sure was new. He wrote, "I may mention one fact which I have not noticed in any work and which appears to me to belong to the same class of phenomenon as those before described." He had noticed that when the terminals of a battery were connected by a short wire, say 3 feet long, no spark was to be observed either when the wire was connected or disconnected. However, with a length of 30 or 40 feet of wire there was no spark on connection but a bright spark occurred on breaking the circuit, and the effect was increased by coiling the wire into the form of a helix. He had discovered self-induction, that is, the phenomenon of an "extra current" moving in the opposite direction that opposes the dying out of current. Several years later when he visited London he was to demonstrate this effect to the surprise and great interest of Faraday and others who apparently had not read—or else not understood—Henry's report in 1832.

As a follow-up to his discovery of electromagnetic induction Henry built a small electromagnetic engine. It consisted of a bar of iron about 9 inches long with its end turned over to face two upright magnets. The bar was wound with wire, and the ends of the wire were in two opposite mercury cups, each connected to a separate battery. The arm made about one oscillation a second. Henry had made an electric motor, but he regarded it merely as a "philosophical toy" and did not try to develop it further. He did suggest, however, that the same principle or some modification of it on a more extended scale might be applied to some useful purpose. Rotary motors came a few years later.

In 1832 Henry left Albany Institute to accept the chair of natural philosophy at the College of New Jersey, later renamed Princeton University. During his first two years there he had little time for his scientific researches, but when he did take up investigations again, he had adequate space and better material and equipment for his work.

After settling down at his new position Henry continued his work on electromagnets and raised the lifting power of his devices to a ton and a half. But not all his work was with lifting magnets. In 1835 he invented a device for amplifying a weak current. This device, known as a relay, consisted of an electromagnet having a pivoted armature with which was associated a pair of contacts. The magnet was wound with many turns of wire. Thus a weak current arriving from a distance, as in a telegraph circuit, reproduced the signals by means of a local battery and, so reinforced, passed them on to a further section of the line. He also produced a noninductive winding for resistance coils by doubling the wire back on itself halfway. Both these inventions are still in use today.

In 1836 the trustees of the college granted Henry a year's leave of absence on full salary to visit Europe. After a crossing of more than eighteen days he landed at Plymouth, England, where he called on Sir William Snow Harris, who was famous for his electrostatic experiments.

He then traveled by coach to London, stopping on the way to see the ancient remains at Stonehenge by moonlight.

In London Henry found lodging in Jermyn Street near Piccadilly Circus and within easy reach of the Royal Institution, the Royal Society, and King's College. During his visit he met William Sturgeon, whose electromagnet had inspired some of his most important investigations, and he sat in on one of Faraday's lectures. At King's College he spent many hours in the laboratory working on electrical experiments, mainly with Faraday, Charles Wheatstone—a well-known professor of physics at the college—and John Daniell. During one of Henry's laboratory visits the three English scientists were experimenting with a thermopile consisting of two wires of different metals joined together in which current was produced by heating the junction remote from the open ends.

In turn, each of the three Englishmen attempted to produce a spark by touching the wires together. After all three had failed, Henry tried. Taking a longer piece of wire, he made it into a coil which he added to one of the wires that was being joined. By thus increasing the inductance in the circuit he was able to draw a momentary spark when, after contact, he separated the two ends. What he had done was to apply a principle he had explained in his 1832 paper on electromagnetic inductance. Whether or not Faraday had read Henry's paper, the idea was new to him. He was delighted and in his excitement cried out, "Hurrah for the Yankee experiment."

From London Henry went to Paris, where he remarked on "eating in the street, women sitting on the sidewalks in groups sewing and talking as freely as if they were in their own houses . . ." and other curious habits of the French. He met a number of scientists, including Auguste Arthur de la Rive, Joseph Gay-Lussac, and Jean Baptiste Biot, but did not hold the members of the French Institute in very high esteem as "they read their newspapers during the presentation of a scientific paper."

After two months in Paris and in nearby countries on the Continent, Henry returned to London. From there he made a trip to Scotland, where he visited the astronomer Sir David Brewster and other scientists, and then went to see his mother's relatives in Ayrshire.

On his return to Princeton in 1837 Henry resumed his electromagnetic experiments. He added refinements to many of his earlier discoveries and issued reports on his results. He originated the step-down and step-up transformers by an experiment which "established the fact that an 'intensity' current of [high voltage] can induce one of 'quantity' [more current of lower voltage] and . . . that a 'quantity' current can induce one of 'intensity.' "

One of his discoveries that had fundamental importance in the development of electrical theory was that the discharge of a Leyden jar was not continuous but oscillatory. He also made a comparison between the spread of an electric impulse to the transmission of light waves and reported experiments in which he had induced electric current in coils of wire that were completely separated from the electric spark.

This report on the propagation of electromagnetic (radio) waves through space was verified later by the scientists Clerk Maxwell and Heinrich Hertz. Guglielmo Marconi, who invented the wireless telegraph in the 1890's, included the name of Joseph Henry among those who had paved the way for his accomplishment.

Henry gave up his work in electromagnetism in the early 1840's. At the time he wrote that his "several thousand original investigations on electricity, magnetism, and electro magnetism" had cost him "years of labor and much expense." During the mid-1840's he investigated other scientific fields, including phosphorescence, the solution of one metal in another, the structure of bubbles, and other subjects. He became interested in atmospheric electricity, studied thunderstorms and sunsets, and constructed a piece of apparatus that measured the heat radiated from a man a mile away.

On December 3, 1846, at the age of forty-nine, Henry accepted an invitation to become secretary of the newly founded Smithsonian Institution at Washington, D.C. He held this position for the next thirty-two years and had more to do with the Institution's development than any man except James Smithson, who gave it his money and his name.

Born in 1765, Smithson was the illegitimate son of the first Duke of Northumberland and, through his mother, was a direct descendant of King Henry VII of England. Although a science graduate of Oxford and, later, a Fellow of the Royal Society, he was cold-shouldered by London society because of the circumstances of his birth. He then moved to France, where his house in Paris became a center of hospitality for scientific friends and cultured American visitors.

When Smithson died in 1829 he left his fortune—"a sum of 105,960 golden sovereigns and eight shillings and seven pence wrapped in paper"—to the United States of America, in the event of his nephew dying without heirs. The money was to be used "to found at Washington, under the name of the Smithsonian Institution, an establishment for the increase and diffusion of knowledge among men." Smithson undoubtedly overlooked England in his bequest out of resentment for his treatment there, and chose the United States as the location for his institution through the influence of some of his American friends.

When the United States Government was presented with the bequest after the death of Smithson's nephew in 1835, the American officials were not sure what to do about it. Congress spent nine years debating whether to accept the money and considering such questions as what was meant by the "increase and diffusion of knowledge among men." Meanwhile, appeals came from many quarters to make the money available for observatories, libraries, colleges, museums, lecture courses, and so on. Finally the Institution was established by an Act of Congress, a Board of Regents was set up, and Joseph Henry appointed to head the new organization.

From the earliest discussions of it, Henry had taken a lively interest in the Smithson bequest and his proposed plan for the Institution received full approval by the Regents. His acceptance of the post was not entirely approved by many of his friends, who feared that the burden of his administrative duties would cause him to abandon laboratory work and scientific writing. Their worry was well grounded, for after his appointment Henry had little time for research.

However, his work as head of the Smithsonian brought him as much renown as his scientific work, and he proved to be a good administrator who was able to translate the founder's intentions for stimulating research and disseminating knowledge into a program of action. As head of the Smithsonian he defended the integrity of its operations and resisted efforts to squander the fund that would have hampered its future activities. The story of his leadership of the Institution is told in the volumes of the Smithsonian's annual reports.

Henry lived to be about eighty and remained active and quite healthy almost to the day of his death on May 13, 1878. One of the most warming tributes to his work was offered by a doctor whom he consulted a few months before he died. When Henry asked, "How much do I owe you?" the doctor replied, "You are not in my debt. There are no debts for the Dean of American Science."

9
GEORG SIMON OHM
1789-1854

When the Royal Society awarded Georg Simon Ohm its highest distinction, the Copley Medal, for his researches into the laws of the electric circuit, the citation indicated that "he had clarified in a remarkable way what had been previously wrapped in mystery and confusion." Even Joseph Henry had not really understood the nature of the difference between what he called "intensity" and "quantity" current. Henry had been aware, however, that different kinds of electrical setups were involved in producing the two types of electrical force. A " quantity" type of circuit—a short, thick wire—called for a "quantity" type of battery, such as a single cell with large plates. An "intensity" type of load—for instance, an electromagnet with many turns of wire, or a long telegraph line—required an "intensity" type of battery, one with many cells in series.

It was Ohm who developed the simple law to explain the behavior of electric circuits. This law states that the current flowing is proportional to the sum of the electromotive forces acting in the circuit divided by the sum of the resist-

GEORG SIMON OHM

ances. Algebraically this is represented by the expression

$$\text{current} = \frac{E}{R} \left(\frac{\text{electromotive} = \text{force of battery}}{\text{resistance}} \right)$$

It is difficult for us today to understand why it was necessary for any man to spend so much thought and so many years of his life discovering such a simple relationship; now it is understood and used by schoolboys, and in its many extended forms it is taken for granted and used widely in the science and practice of electrical engineering.

Georg Simon Ohm was born on March 16, 1789, at Erlangen in Bavaria. His father and his father's father were locksmiths, and his mother, who died when he was ten, was the daughter of a tailor named Beckin. The oldest of seven children, Ohm had a brother Martin who became a distinguished mathematician at the Military College in Berlin.

In Erlangen a tablet on a modest house at No. 6 Fahrstrasse states that Georg Simon Ohm and his brother Martin were born there. It is not certain that this is true although records show that a family named Ohm lived at numbers 11 and 20 Fahrstrasse at about the time of the brother's birth.

The two boys studied with their scholarly father when they were young and received encouragement from a Professor Langsdorff, their father's friend. Georg later spent a year in the Erlangen gymnasium, and then entered the university in that town but he remained only three terms because of lack of funds. At eighteen he was appointed tutor of mathematics at a school in Switzerland, where, in spite of his rather unprepossessing appearance, he made a good impression because of his ability.

After he had spent some time teaching and studying mathematics privately he returned to his birthplace. There, at the University of Erlangen, he received the degree of Doctor of Philosophy at the age of twenty-two. He tried to find a good teaching position in mathematics and physics, but his poverty finally forced him to take a tutoring job at a school in Bamberg. Although the working conditions were not to his liking, he stayed there for some six years. During this time he finished his first book on geometry as an educational aid.

As was often done in those days, Ohm sent copies of the book to various reigning monarchs in the hope of getting help to advance his career. One copy went to King Wilhelm III of Prussia, who was impressed and offered him a teaching post in mathematics and physics at a Jesuit college in Cologne, the principal place of instruction for Catholic youth in the Rhineland.

During his nine years at Cologne, Ohm began to specialize in the study of the electric circuit. He investigated the conductivity of metals and the many interesting developments of the galvanometer, but the subject that fascinated him most was the theory of the electric circuit itself. He was granted a year's leave of absence from his teaching duties and concentrated entirely on his investigation of the circuit. Living in his brother's house in Berlin, he used his time so profitably that within twelve months he had completed his great work, *The Galvanic Circuit Investigated Mathematically,* which was published in May 1827.

In his introduction to the *Bibliographical History of Electricity and Magnetism* by Mottelay, the celebrated English professor Silvanus P. Thompson recommended "the careful examination of the actual ways in which the discoveries of science, now facts of history, were actually made" and as an example said, "Let him [the student] read Ohm's own account of the law of the circuit."

Ohm's paper, which consisted of over a hundred pages and several diagrams, was translated into English from the German. It was published in London in 1841 and in New York in 1891.

The theory of the circuit that Ohm developed in this paper was likened by the great German scientist Kohlrausch to "a pole star illuminating the obscurity in which men of science had groped for many years."

His success in solving the baffling problem of the circuit depended on his realization that it must be considered in terms of the whole setup of wires and battery and not just as the wire external to the battery, as others had thought. He was, then, the first to show that the opposition to the flow of current consisted of two portions, that of the magnet coil, galvanometer, or long telegraph wire *and* that of the battery. As Kohlrausch pointed out, "At a stroke the difficulties which up to that time had beset the subject and which had been thought insuperable by those who had confined their attention to the exterior resistance only, crumbled away."

In the introduction to his famous paper, Ohm requested the "well-disposed reader to receive the performance with the same love for the object as that with which it is sent forth." His own enthusiasm for his investigation is evident in his careful selection of experiments and his overwhelming assembly of arguments.

During his study of the circuit, Ohm decided that chemical batteries were too unreliable for his experiments. To obtain a more steady supply of electrical potential he adopted the thermoelectric junction, or thermocouple, as it is called. This type of junction brings together two dissimilar metals which maintain a difference of potential when heated at the point of contact. To complete his circuit he decided to use a ring of uniform wire connected to the thermocouple.

The 1822 study of the French scientist Baron Jean Baptiste Joseph Fourier on the diffusion of heat probably influenced Ohm's thinking regarding the operation of the circuit. He came to the conclusion that the way electricity was transmitted along a wire would be similar to the way that heat was transmitted along a solid object after a steady state had been reached, that is, when heat was traveling at a uniform rate through all parts of the object. Fourier had shown that the transmission of heat depended on the difference in temperature between one part and another. Applying the same idea to electricity, Ohm concluded that the current in the circuit would be proportional to the difference in electric potential and that a current having the same magnitude at all points in a uniform wire would produce a uniform drop in potential along the wire. He produced a mathematical analysis of this effect and checked the results by practical experiment.

In constructing diagrams to illustrate the transmission of current he imagined the ring of wire laid out straight. He showed how the positive potential at the end of the wire in contact with the positive pole of the thermojunction fell away to zero halfway along the circuit. Beyond the halfway point in the wire the negative potential began to build up until it reached the full negative potential at the point connected with the negative pole of the battery.

He then considered how the building up and dropping off

of this potential would be affected by changes in the size of the wire used in different sections. In diagrams and algebraic formulas, he illustrated the changes that would result. He also analyzed the distribution of current between conducting paths when two wires were connected separately to the thermojunction—that is, in parallel.

In page after page of his report he brought up new variations in the setup of circuits and explained how each condition would affect the transmission of the current. Although modern knowledge has taken us much further in understanding the subject, his report is still sufficient to give a reader of it a basic comprehension of what is involved in the operation of electric circuits.

At the time there was much confusion regarding the measurement of current. Some otherwise reliable scientists were misinterpreting the effect of current on a suspended bar galvanometer. They were making the mistake of overlooking the difference between the sudden violent deflection of the galvanometer that occurred the moment the current was turned on and the steady deflection produced by an unchanging current. Ohm recognized the importance of waiting until the galvanometer registered a steady state. His use of a thermojunction helped him in obtaining reliable measurements because it produced a current which did not fall off as did that from the crude chemical batteries then ordinarily used.

Ohm also appreciated the often overlooked fact that the angle through which a galvanometer magnet moved was not itself a true measure of the current in the deflecting coil. When the galvanometer was registering a large angle of deflection it was less affected by a given increase in current. To obtain a truer measure of the current he constructed a torsion device by suspending a small galvanometer magnet at the end of a flat gold strip. When this suspended magnet was deflected by the current in the fixed coil it could be brought back to zero by twisting the head of the suspension. At each reading of the instrument, the magnet always had the same position relative to the coil. Thus there was no need to introduce trigonometrical correction to take into account differences in the influence of the earth's magnetic field when the magnet was deflected at different angles in relation to the field.

In his paper Ohm described how he used the gold-leaf electroscope to measure the potential at any point in the circuit. From the name given to this device in the days when it was used in electrostatic experiments he adopted the term "electroscopic force" to designate the originating force which causes an electric current. Today the term "electromotive force" is used for this quantity.

Ohm also had to find a way of designating the opposition offered to the passage of electricity by batteries, thermojunctions, and galvanometers—by all items in the circuit other than the wire itself. He expressed the amount of resistance in terms of "reduced length." Each unit of reduced length was equivalent to a stated number of feet of the copper wire he was using to connect the circuit. Today, units of resistance are expressed in terms of "ohms."

When Ohm's report appeared in 1827 it met with a mixed reception. One of the scientists who recognized its importance was Joseph Henry, whose knowledge of the subject made him a more reliable judge than most of his contemporaries. Henry wrote that when he first read Ohm's theory

". . . a light arose within me like the sudden illumination of a dark room by lightning." Another of Ohm's supporters was Charles Wheatstone in England, who commented that ". . . there is scarcely any branch of experimental science in which so many and such various phenomena are expressed as formulae of such simplicity and generality . . . what has hitherto been more matter of speculative conjecture is removed into the domain of positive philosophy." In France also the scientific circles were impressed favorably enough to concede that his work would have been worthy of their country.

Unfortunately, in his own land, where it mattered most to him, Ohm ran into a great deal of skepticism and criticism. In Germany at that time the new philosophy of Hegel was coming into fashion and the process of scientific research as a means to determine truth was being challenged. Ohm's ideas and procedures were not in step with the trend of German thought and his work was ridiculed. Even the authorities of his school at Cologne gave him to understand that he was no longer welcome on the faculty. Having no other alternative, he resigned and retired into private life.

After Ohm had wasted nearly six years in idleness, misery, and resentment, his fortunes took a turn for the better. He received an appointment to teach at the Polytechnic School at Nuremberg, where he remained for the next twenty years. Gradually the world began to realize how great was his contribution to electrical science. When he was in his fifties the Royal Society of England finally awarded him their highest honor, the Copley Medal. Ohm was deeply moved by this gesture of appreciation from a foreign country. He began to lose his resentment over the way his countrymen had treated him and turned once more to research and writing.

During the latter part of his life Ohm received many honors and favors. He was given the chair of mathematics at his old university in Cologne and received an important government appointment as State Inspector of Scientific Education. Later he reached the rektor's chair at Nuremberg, and finally, at the age of sixty, he was given the position that he had particularly wanted: he was made a professor at the University of Munich, where he became involved in many administrative duties. He had been at Munich only a few years when he died suddenly of apoplexy on July 6, 1854.

Ohm never married. He lived an isolated life, but was kind to others and beloved by his students. Not a great talker, he was always to the point, thus reflecting the quality of precision that was also notable in his scientific work. At a meeting in Paris in 1881, members of the Electrical Congress paid him one of the highest compliments they could grant to a fellow scientist. They adopted the "ohm" as an international standard of electrical resistance.

10

KARL FRIEDRICH GAUSS
1777-1855

WILHELM EDUARD WEBER
1804-1891

These two remarkable men are placed together because of their mutual contribution to a phase of electrical science of great fundamental significance, the system of absolute units. They also share the credit of constructing a pioneer electromagnetic telegraph system.

Gauss, one of the world's outstanding mathematicians and primarily an astronomer, carried out a profound investigation of the earth's magnetism in which he reduced the quantities involved to absolute measure. In this he laid the foundation on which subsequent generations of investigators, in all branches of electrical science, have erected a magnificent and comprehensive structure of absolute and practical units for all electrical and magnetic quantities. Without this progress in theoretical research the practical applications of electricity would have been impossible. Among the end products of this development are these familiar units—the volt, the unit of electromotive force or pressure; the ampere, the

KARL FRIEDRICH GAUSS

WILHELM WEBER

unit of electric current; and the ohm, the unit of electrical resistance. Later we will take a look at the steps by which Gauss's early inspiration led to extensive use of units in electrical measurement in the present day.

Weber was professor of physics at the University of Göttingen when Gauss, who was twenty-seven years his senior, carried on work in a nearby observatory. He cooperated with Gauss in his magnetic tests. He had, however, followed closely the discoveries of Oersted, Ampère, and Faraday and saw the possibilities of extending Gauss's ideas to current electricity. Gauss's first publication on the theory of magnetism, "Review of Absolute Measurements of Terrestrial Magnetism," appeared in 1833, and three years later the two men collaborated in a report on the results of a large number of magnetic tests. This cooperation was the beginning of a long series of investigations into electrical units and measurements. Before he died, Weber saw the completion of the system which had occupied the greater part of his working life.

Karl Friedrich Gauss was born at Braunschweig, in central Germany, on April 30, 1777. His father, a stonemason with a variety of other occupations, including keeping the books of a burial fund, lived until his son was about thirty. Gauss's mother, Dorothea, was a native of Velpke, twenty miles north of Braunschweig. She was a woman of strong character, intelligent, and sympathetic. From his childhood until his mother's death at the age of ninety-seven, Gauss kept in close touch with her and always spoke of her with great affection. When in her last years she became blind, she lived with him in his observatory at Göttingen. It is said that to the end she kept her country dialect and manners.

The house where Gauss spent his boyhood, located in what is now the Wilhelmstrasse section in Braunschweig, is marked by a tablet. In his time the house stood beside a canal which was filled in many years ago.

Almost from his babyhood it was evident that Gauss was unusually gifted, particularly in the handling of figures. He learned about numbers by studying an old calendar, and later in life joked that he could calculate before he could speak. Once when he was three years old he was watching his father paying workmen their wages and called attention to an error in the calculation for overtime.

In elementary school he showed such skill in calculating that the schoolmaster let him work with a mathematically inclined young assistant named Bartels. The arrangement helped Gauss develop a mathematical skill far beyond that of most boys his age. According to one of the stories about his early school days, he once asked to take part in an arithmetic examination for boys of fourteen or fifteen. His audacity annoyed the schoolmaster, who decided to let him have his way and experience the humiliation of failure. Gauss worked a few minutes on the examination problem and then laid down his slate with the correct answer. "Here it is," he called. By the time he was ten, Gauss was working with the binomial theorem and infinite series.

As he was growing up his family became prosperous enough to send him to high school where he acquired some knowledge of Latin and Greek and won a reputation for outstanding mathematical ability. When he was fourteen two prominent men in the town became interested in him and called him to the notice of the Duke Carl W. Ferdinand of Braunschweig. With the duke's patronage, Gauss was able to enroll at the Collegium Carolinum. His old friend and teacher, Bartels, had preceded him there as a student and eventually became a professor.

At sixteen, while he was attending the Collegium Carolinum, Gauss published his first papers. When he was eighteen he transferred to the university at Göttingen. At the time of the move his interest in classical and modern languages competed with his mathematical studies, but at Göttingen the "queen of sciences," as he called mathematics, completely lured him from other fields of study. While he was there he began the series of mathematical discoveries which were to make him famous in later years. During his first year he demonstrated the method of least squares. Soon afterward he solved a complex problem in the subdivision of the circle which his university teacher, a man of some distinction, had asserted was insoluble. Throughout his life he set a high value on this last discovery.

In 1801 Gauss published, after some years' delay, his famous "Arithmetical Disquisitions." At the time he was twenty-four, and during the preparation of this work he stayed in Helmstedt at the home of Professor Johann Friedrich Pfaff, who is famous for his work on the solution of differential equations. During the same year Gauss became interested in astronomy after hearing about the discovery of a new body in the solar system. The body, the first asteroid to be detected by man, was found by Giuseppi Piazzi, an astronomer at the University of Palermo, who named it Ceres after the patron deity of Sicily. In the two months it took for the news to be publicized, the asteroid changed its position and other astronomers could not locate it to confirm the discovery. However, Gauss devised a method of calculating its orbit. Because he was able to predict its reappearance and position, the asteroid was located during the following December. When Gauss's prediction was confirmed his reputation was greatly enhanced. He received many offers of appointments and, in 1807, at the age of thirty, he became director of the observatory at Göttingen.

On October 9, 1805, Gauss had married Johanne Osthof of Braunschweig, who died four years later at the birth of her third child. Soon after his wife's death, Gauss became involved in the establishment of a new observatory at Göttingen, a project which took nine years.

While he was busy with the observatory, Gauss also continued his work in mathematics. During this period he developed a method for calculating the distribution of errors which is much used by statisticians. He also conducted a trigonometrical survey of the Hanoverian kingdom in Germany using formulas of his own devising that are still used in spherical trigonometry.

One of Gauss's surveying inventions was his heliotrope, a controlled movable mirror to catch the sun's rays which later led to the development of the modern heliostat. Since the reflection from this device could be seen from far away, surveyors used it for marking distant points in triangulation surveys. Gauss actually toyed with the idea of communicating with possible inhabitants on the moon by means of the instrument and calculated the required size of the mirror which would be necessary.

Although mathematics was always Gauss's prime preoccupation, he liked to venture into other fields of study, particularly if they lent themselves to the application of mathematics. He kept little notebooks filled with information on such subjects as the life-spans of men of importance and of deceased friends, the monthly receipts of the Hanoverian railways, and the distances from the observatory to places he visited frequently. He was interested in mortality tables, liked to follow the stock market, and held strong opinions on state credit and paper money. His principal recreation was reading, and his choice of books ranged widely in subject and language. In English he admired the novelist Sir Walter Scott and the historians Edward Gibbon and Thomas Macaulay, and read all their main works. He read the leading newspapers of the world and followed political events closely. A conservative, he preferred the absolute rule of an intelligent elite and was horrified by the excesses of mob rule in the French Revolution. He always took great pains to harmonize his scientific experience with his personal philosophy.

Among the subjects that interested Gauss was the progress of electrical science. There is evidence that as early as 1806, when he was twenty-nine, he had formulated a theory of magnetism, but he did not publish it. It was not until 1828 that Gauss's career really became involved with electricity. All that he did in the field is closely associated with Wilhelm Weber, whom he met that year at a conference in Berlin.

Wilhelm Eduard Weber was born on October 24, 1804, at Wittenberg in Saxony. His father, a professor of theology at the university there, held the same position Martin Luther had held three centuries earlier. Wilhelm was the fifth in a family of seven children, and two of his brothers also became scientists.

When Weber was a boy in Wittenberg the town was suffering the effects of the Napoleonic wars and his family was living in great poverty. In spite of this his father managed to give him a basic education. When Weber was eleven years old the University of Wittenberg was absorbed by the University of Halle and the Weber family moved with it. In Halle, Wilhelm was sent to the Orphanage School, and, at eighteen, matriculated at the university there.

While Wilhelm was a university student he and his brother Ernst, who was ten years his senior, carried out experiments to investigate wave motion. In 1825 the brothers collaborated in publishing a book on the subject.

Wilhelm Weber received his doctor's degree in 1827. For a short time after his graduation he lectured in the university as a *privat docent*—a member of the faculty paid directly by the students—and soon received an appointment as assistant professor of natural philosophy. By the time he was twenty-four he had made his mark in the scientific world and was appointed a corresponding member of the Royal Academy of Sciences in Turin. It was at about this time that he met Gauss, who recommended him for a position at his university.

In 1831 Weber went to Göttingen to occupy the chair of physics. He organized a physics laboratory and established an important series of experimental lectures. He and Gauss, who was working in the observatory only fifteen minutes away, saw a great deal of each other and a friendly rivalry sprang up between them. At the time, Gauss had been formulating mathematically a method of measuring the earth's magnetic field at a given point. By joining forces with Weber, who was a practical instrument maker, he was able to carry out the large number of tests that were suggested by his mathematical analysis.

For the tests, Weber constructed a magnetometer to measure the strengths of magnetic fields, in particular the magnetic field of the earth. His very simple instrument consisted of a small magnetic needle suspended by a fine thread over a graduated circular scale. To increase the sensitivity of the readings he attached a long light pointer at right angles to the needle. Later he replaced the pointer with a device that is now well known, a tiny mirror attached to the needle and from which a beam of light was reflected to shine on a stationary scale. Another of his refinements was the addition of long, straight wooden graduated scales at the opposite sides of the circular compass case. Each scale was furnished with a groove along which a bar magnet could be slid to any required distance from the needle.

In making his measurements of the earth's magnetic field, Gauss divided the process into two steps. As his first step he placed the magnetometer with the needle pointing north and south. Then he brought up the bar magnet in the slot lying east and west, and in this way obtained a deflection of the needle. The angle of the needle's deflection was written down along with the distance of the sliding magnet from the needle. By applying his theoretical formulas he was able to calculate the value of the ratio M/H where M represented the unknown magnetic properties of the magnet and H represented the value of the earth's field which he was seeking to determine.

To get around his ignorance of the value of M—the so-called moment of the magnet—Gauss employed a clever but simple mathematical procedure. His method of setting up the problem involved another measurement. For this he suspended the magnet in a stirrup on a long supporting thread, rotated it through an angle out of the natural north-south direction, and let it go. It oscillated from east through north to west and back again in the earth's field, backward and forward, slowly coming to rest. He noted the time of a complete oscillation and, by applying one of his formulas and simple algebra to this figure, he obtained the value of the product MH. Having the values for both M/H and MH he was able to cancel out the M component and determine accurately the value of H, the earth's field. Gauss's "Review of Absolute Measurements of Terrestrial Magnetism" appeared in 1833.

For several years after this procedure had been worked out, Gauss and Weber occupied themselves with taking measurements of the earth's magnetic field in different parts of the country. As an outgrowth of their work, a magnetic association was formed which published a valuable collection of papers on the result. The measurements also provided the data for one of Weber's most important works, an atlas of terrestrial magnetism.

About the year 1833, Gauss and Weber decided that they should improve communication between the university physics laboratory and the observatory. To this end they jointly devised an electromagnetic telegraph. At first they obtained their current from a galvanic battery but later they used an induction device based on Faraday's recent discovery. The transmitting key itself generated the current which, at the receiving end, passed through a coil of wire and deflected a magnetic needle. The telegraph signals were received in the form of a beam of light reflected from a mirror attached to the needle. Weber, at the same time, was collaborating with his younger brother Eduard in physio-physi-

COURTESY BURNDY LIBRARY

The Gauss-Weber telegraph.

cal experiments. One of the subjects they investigated was the mechanics of the human walking process, and the brothers were coauthors of a book on the subject.

While Weber and Gauss were working with their telegraph, political changes were occurring in the kingdom of Hanover (where Göttingen was located) that were destined to upset Weber's career. In 1833 the Hanoverians had succeeded in ridding themselves of a very repressive constitution that had been in effect since 1819, but in 1837 a new and reactionary ruler revived the 1819 constitution. As "King's Servants," the staff of the university at Göttingen were called upon to comply with the restored constitution. Gauss was able to do so without offending his convictions, but Weber and six other professors refused to comply and on December 14, 1837, they were relieved of their rights and privileges. The dismissal of the seven professors stirred wide interest in Germany, and a subscription was taken up for them. As his share of this fund Weber received a sum equal to two years' salary.

Through the influence of well-placed friends, Weber was able to remain in Göttingen, where he continued to work with Gauss and on his own projects. During this period he also did some traveling and visited several countries, including England. After four years of this enforced retirement his need for money caused him to accept a post in the University of Leipzig. The new position had the advantage of bringing him in close touch with his brothers Ernst and Eduard. In addition, he was able to set up a magnetic observatory in a building that was iron-free, a condition which was very good for his electromagnetic experiments. One of the products of his work in Leipzig was his publication "General Basis of Electrical Effects." Another was the electrodynamometer that he invented in 1843. This invention was a galvanometer for measuring the strength of a current by its interaction with another current and consisted of a small coil suspended inside a larger fixed coil. The means of suspension was by two fine wires close together, which gave the smaller coil stability yet allowed it to turn as its own current interacted with the current in the larger coil. Thus when the coils were in series with one another and the current flowed through both, the deflection, with a simple trigonometrical correction, was proportional to the square of the current in the two coils.

After another revolution in 1848 Hanover returned to a more liberal political rule and Weber resumed his chair at the University of Göttingen. By this time his friend Gauss was in his seventies, although he was still actively engaged and retained his meticulous attention to detail. Their working relationship ended when Gauss died on February 23, 1855, at the age of seventy-eight.

In the 1850's and after, Weber applied himself to the main work of his career. Twenty years earlier Gauss had considered that electrical science needed absolute units to measure electrical quantities. His suggestion inspired Weber to undertake the painstaking job of working out a coherent and exact system of measurement. The significance of this work is best appreciated when we consider how the three main electrical quantities—electromotive force, nowadays measured in volts; resistance, measured in ohms; and current, measured in amperes—were dealt with when Weber undertook to systematize the units of measurement. At the time there were no accepted standard units as are now so widely used.

In the search for a standard of electromotive force it seemed obvious that the one adopted should be based on the value obtained from a particular form of battery, but most of the batteries used then did not provide a steady value of electromotive force. However, there was one that gave a more reliable performance, developed by an English scientist, John Daniell, in 1836. His battery was based on a two-fluid principle. It had a zinc plate in dilute sulphuric acid and a copper plate in a solution of copper sulphate which were separated by a porous material. The value given by one such cell became the widely accepted standard for electromotive force and was adopted by Weber in his own system.

An exact knowledge of the resistance of a circuit became

especially important when telegraphy was being developed for practical use in the 1830's and '40's. As early as 1833, Lenz, a German physicist, decided arbitrarily to use the resistance encountered in 1 foot of No. 11 copper wire as a unit. Charles Wheatstone, closely associated with early telegraph development, later proposed a different way of expressing the unit. He adopted one based on the resistance of a foot of copper wire weighing 100 grains. By 1848 there were twenty or more alternative ways of expressing resistance. In England, the unit was based on 1 mile of No. 16 copper wire; in France, on 1 kilometer of copper wire 4 millimeters in diameter; and, in Germany, on a German mile of No. 8 iron wire. One must remember that, apart from the inconvenience involved in dealing with all the samples of wire at that date, the resistance of copper itself varied from 100 per cent down to 14 per cent, depending on the source and treatment of the copper. It was evident to Weber that these arbitrary units of voltage resistance and current must be replaced by an absolute system of units, and he started on the unit of current. He studied the earlier experiments of Ampère, who had demonstrated that such a current produced a magnetic effect outside the wire. The magnitude of the effect varied not only with the strength of the current but with the length of wire and the distance from the wire. He therefore took the obvious decision that a unit current should be taken as that current which produced a unit of force on a unit magnetic pole placed at a unit distance from the wire.

The piece of apparatus which enabled these different quantities to be related to one another was the tangent galvanometer—in essence a circular coil of large diameter fixed with its axis horizontal and at right angles to the earth's magnetic field. At the center of the coil was suspended a compass needle with a long light pointer. When the coil carried no current the needle pointed north and south—that is, in the plane of the coil. When a current flowed in the coil, the earth's magnetic field was partly overcome by the field due to the current, and the needle was deflected until a balance was obtained.

Now as we have seen from his earlier work with Gauss, Weber could determine the strength of the earth's magnetic field independently so that by using this figure and taking the dimensions of the coil, the number of turns of wire, and the angle of deflection he had only to pass the current through a solution of silver on its way to the coil and weigh the amount of silver deposited. Then he had complete knowledge of the value of the current which could be accurately reproduced at any time.

Weber next turned his attention to the determination of an absolute unit of electrical resistance and produced an equally elegant device. He set up a coil of wire on trunnions so that it could be spun in the earth's magnetic field by means of a cord and pulley. At the center of the coil of wire was fixed a pivoted magnetic needle. When the coil was rotated, a current was generated in the winding and this in turn acted on the compass needle against its normal deflection. By simple calculation of dimensions, speed of rotation, and actual deflection, the absolute value of the resistance of the coil could be calculated.

Without going into detail, what Weber did in working out the values of electrical units was to relate them to the physical units of length, mass, and time. For example, he expressed electrical resistance in terms of length and time, or as a velocity.

The establishment of the absolute system of electrical units created a great deal of interest in all countries. International committees were established to check the results and increase the accuracy of determination. In this work, which has continued up to the present, Weber participated almost until his death in Göttingen on June 23, 1891. He was eighty-six when he died and had remained physically and mentally very active almost to the end.

11

JAMES CLERK MAXWELL
1831-1879

Although the name of James Clerk Maxwell usually calls to mind his work on the theory of electromagnetism, he made experimental and mathematical contributions to many other fields of science. During his short life—he died at forty-eight—he published a hundred or more papers that contained new ideas about a variety of scientific subjects.

As one example, Maxwell's investigations of the distribution of faster- and slower-moving particles in gases explained how pressure and heat are produced through the collision of the particles. Working in the field of astronomy, he spent two years studying the rings of Saturn and then advanced the theory that they were neither solid nor liquid but were composed of an indefinite number of unconnected particles revolving around the planet.

His scientific genius was recognized in his own day as well as afterward. A famous astronomer of his time, Sir George Airy, said that Maxwell's work represented the most remarkable application of mathematics he had ever seen. Sir James Jeans, an astronomer and physicist of later fame, called him "the greatest physicist the world has seen since Newton."

It is not surprising that a few years later William Hop-

JAMES CLERK MAXWELL

kins, his coach at Cambridge, described him as unquestionably the most extraordinary man he had ever met in the whole range of his experience. It appeared impossible, Hopkins said, for Maxwell to think incorrectly on physical subjects.

From the standpoint of electrical history, Maxwell's mathematical theory of electricity and magnetism did a great deal to advance the development of electricity as an exact science and as a practical source of energy. As a by-product, his theory applied to the behavior of light as well as electricity. Maxwell also edited the papers of Cavendish and was directly responsible for building up experimental physics at Cambridge University and for founding the famous Cavendish Laboratory there.

James Clerk Maxwell was born in Edinburgh, Scotland, on June 13, 1831. His father was a lawyer of Scottish descent who took his profession lightly and devoted much of his time to restoring the family seat located some sixteen miles west of Dumfries, Scotland. It was at this house, called Glenlair, that Maxwell spent his early years.

Maxwell's father, besides his interest in his home, had a strong curiosity about the way things were made. He never lost an opportunity to examine manufactured items and visit interesting buildings, and he passed this interest on to his young son. A question the boy was always asking was, "What's the go of that?" If the answer did not satisfy his desire for an explanation he would ask again, "But what's the particular go of that?"

At the age of eight Maxwell lost his mother. However, in the years before her death, she had encouraged her son to "look up through nature to God" and guided his reading in the Scriptures and in poetry. All his life Maxwell was deeply religious, although he never liked to discuss his feelings about it, and he always remembered the passages and poems he had learned as a boy. He also wrote verse of his own.

After his mother died, Maxwell was placed in the hands of a tutor. The arrangement did not work out satisfactorily and, at the end of two years, he was sent to stay with an aunt in Edinburgh so that he could attend the Edinburgh Academy. In getting him outfitted for school, Maxwell's father did not follow the fashions of the time, and Maxwell's schoolmates made fun of his clothes. At the end of his first day he came home with "tunic in rags and wanting skirt, his neat frill rumpled and torn—himself excessively amused by his experiences."

Although his schoolmates called him "Dafty" and teased him for a while, they soon began to admire his agility and strength, his courage, and his good nature. He also impressed his teachers by paying attention to his studies. While he was boarding with his aunt he spent weekends with his father, who took him out on sightseeing expeditions. One trip that Maxwell remembered as a special treat was made in February 1842 when the boy and his father went to see electromagnetic machines.

Between their visits, Maxwell and his father wrote to each other often. Maxwell's letters, which are still preserved, tell of his growing interest in geometry. When he was thirteen he mentioned his mathematical studies for the first time: "I have made a tetrahedron, a dodecahedron, and two other hedrons whose names I don't know," he wrote. Later he began to study curves and their focal points and worked on a method of drawing a perfect oval with a loop of string carried around two fixed pins. While attending meetings of the

Royal Society of Edinburgh with his father he met a Professor Forbes, who was so impressed by the ingenuity and originality of this work that he submitted a paper by Maxwell at one of the meetings. The paper, written when the boy was barely fifteen, received great attention and praise and appeared in the *Proceedings* of the Society dated April 6, 1846.

Maxwell's mathematical interests were also evident in some of the games he liked. He achieved astonishing skill at one called diabolo, or devil, in which a double cone is made to spin on a string extending between two sticks held in the hands. When the device is made to rotate at a speed high enough to achieve the striking properties peculiar to the gyroscope, the cones continue to rotate in the same absolute direction in space even when the string is tilted in different directions. Later, Maxwell applied this toy and the zeotrope, or wheel of life, in his scientific work.

Halfway through his course at Edinburgh Academy, Maxwell underwent a sudden change of personality. According to one of his schoolmates, after years of shyness, "he surprised his companions by suddenly becoming one of the most brilliant among them, gaining prizes, and sometimes the highest prizes, for scholarship, mathematics, and English verse."

When he left the academy, Maxwell went to the University of Edinburgh from 1847 to 1850. While there he had the free use of the experimental apparatus of his old friend, Professor Forbes, and he was able to do physical and chemical experiments completely on his own. He also did a great deal of reading on scientific subjects and wrote two important papers on rolling curves and elastic solids.

By the time he moved to Cambridge University in October 1850 he had acquired an immense amount of knowledge, but it was in such a state of disorder that it appalled his private tutor, whose ideas were more methodical. Maxwell had not been at Cambridge very long before he received a scholarship and became one of the "apostles," a group that included the twelve most outstanding students at the university. In 1854 he scored second on the Cambridge Mathematical Tripos, one of the most important student examinations in the field, and tied for first—with the man who topped him in the Tripos—for the Smith's prize, another very coveted honor.

After he left Cambridge, Maxwell taught natural philosophy at Marischal College in Aberdeen, Scotland. Just before he took up the appointment he lost his father, but two years later he gained a wife, Mary Dewar, the daughter of the college principal.

In 1860 Maxwell moved to London to take up a professorship at King's College, where he taught from 1860 to 1865. During his five years with the college he did some of the most important work of his career. He wrote two famous papers, "Physical Lines of Force" and "Dynamical Theory of the Electromagnetic Field," which were published in 1862 and 1864. The second paper contained a revolutionary prediction that light would be found to have an electromagnetic basis. He also took part in discussions of the British Association for the Advancement of Science which led to the fruition of the ideas of Gausss and Weber on absolute units based on mechanical measurements, and he cooperated in the experiments for the precise determination of the absolute unit of electrical resistance which were carried out in the laboratory at King's College.

Besides his many outside activities Maxwell carried out experiments on the viscosity of gases in the attic of his Kensington home. His wife helped by taking over the exhausting job of stoking the fire to heat the gases to a constant temperature. This homework gave him the material for an important lecture he delivered at the Royal Society.

One of Maxwell's friends during these years was Faraday. The two men had corresponded while Maxwell was still in Scotland and when he moved to London they saw each other at meetings in the Royal Institution. At one such meeting Faraday noticed that Maxwell was trying to work his way out of a crowded lecture theater and took advantage of the situation to make a joke about his friend's work with molecules. "Ho, Maxwell," he called, "cannot you get out? If any man can find his way through a crowd it should be you."

With so many other things to do, Maxwell apparently found his teaching duties somewhat irksome. In a letter to another professor in April 1862 he wrote, "I hope you enjoy the absence of pupils. I find that the division of them into smaller classes is a great help to me and to them; but the total oblivion of them for definite intervals is a necessary condition of doing them justice at the proper time." From such remarks of his and the later comments of people who knew him, one might suspect that he was not usually rated as a very good teacher, and that his lectures might have been over the heads of many of his students. Judging from the contents of one public lecture that he delivered before an audience in the University of London Senate House he could be very witty and learned, but on that occasion he missed the point of his talk, which was to explain the operation of the newly invented telephone.

The centenary history of King's College that covers the period when Maxwell was there hints that he had serious shortcomings in his job. It gives the impression that Maxwell may have been asked to resign because of poor teaching performance and inability to keep order in class. There is nothing in the actual records of the college to prove that this was so, but, on the other hand, the records are missing for two of the years when he was there, 1860 and 1865.

Even if he failed with ordinary classes Maxwell seems to have done well with small classes and brilliant students. Sir Ambrose Fleming, the inventor of the thermionic tube, attended Maxwell's lectures as a student when only two or three students were present, and he said that they covered the subject matter very carefully and completely. In all his experimental classes Maxwell showed the sense of fun that he brought into his teaching. For one class experiment he had the students test the electrical resistance of their hands, and the conclusion drawn from the experiment was that men on the rowing crew had the highest resistance.

Whatever the reasons, Maxwell resigned from King's College in 1865 and went back to Glenlair. During the years that followed he produced the greater part of his most famous work, *Electricity and Magnetism*. To keep in touch with his friends and fellow scientists he wrote and received so many letters that a special letter box was set into a rough stone wall near his home for his personal use. He continued to attend meetings of the British Association and was elected president of one of its sections in 1870. As the subject of his presidential address he discussed the relations between mathematics and physics. During this free time of his life he also made a long visit to Italy, where he learned Italian and improved his knowledge of French, German, and Dutch.

Although he was not teaching, Maxwell served as a mathematics examiner at Cambridge. This university, where Isaac Newton had once been a student and teacher, had fallen behind in science by Maxwell's time, and he took it upon himself to overcome the neglect. As a result of his influence, questions on heat and electricity were introduced into the mathematical honors examinations. The new interest in science that he helped to stimulate reached to the governing body of the university, and in 1869 it recommended that Cambridge should have a new chair of physics and a laboratory. The Duke of Devonshire, who was the university's chancellor, donated money for the laboratory, which was given his family name of Cavendish. The name was especially appropriate since it also honored a great eighteenth-century physicist, Henry Cavendish.

Maxwell was offered the new chair in physics and accepted it, although he had some doubts about his ability to fill the position. In 1871 he took up his duties and directed the building of the new Cavendish Laboratory, which was finished in 1874. If he had not been a good teacher before, he certainly tried to be one in his new position. He was very conscientious about his lecturing and his supervision of laboratory work. During the years he occupied the chair of physics he set a tradition of independent student research that has made Cambridge outstanding in science. Students who studied under him learned about the methods of research by carrying out measurements with the scientific instruments used at the time. After this short introductory course, each of them was set to work on a particular research project. One of the investigations carried out in this way was a comparison of units of electrical resistance for the British Association.

While Maxwell was very careful about planning projects for his students, he never spoon-fed them. He believed that each experimenter should find his own way through the difficulties he met, and he also encouraged original research. He often said that "an experimenter may not find what he is looking for, but he may find something else." It is a measure of his success that several of his Cambridge students later became noted scientists.

Maxwell did not have time left in his life to train many students, for his classes were always small, ranging from two or three to about twenty at most, and he lived only five years after the laboratory was completed. Early in 1879 his friends noticed that he was not well. Although he continued his lectures for several months, he spent less and less time at the laboratory, and died on November 5, 1879.

Unlike so many of the giants of electricity, Maxwell did not contribute an original discovery to electrical science. Instead, he advanced the field by explaining and clarifying the experimental results of Faraday. His interest in electricity had started with boyhood experiments, but he did not begin to study it seriously until after his graduation from Cambridge. At that time he wrote to Professor William Thomson (later Lord Kelvin) at Glasgow University seeking his advice on what to read in the field and began a very thorough study of Faraday's *Researches on Electricity*. For Maxwell, the book raised many questions that needed further explanation, and he decided he would develop Faraday's idea about lines of force. Step by step, he worked out a complete theory that applied not only to electricity but to light. His first paper on the subject was published when he was twenty-three and was read to the Cambridge Philosophical Society on December 10, 1855.

To understand the importance of what Maxwell was doing, we must know how Faraday's theory differed from the views that most scientists held at that time. Most of them accepted the idea that electrical effects depended on action at a distance. They ignored the space outside the conducting bodies and made no attempt to explain how electrical effects could be transmitted between separated objects. Faraday, however, called attention to the space. He imagined it as filled with invisible lines of force that spread out in all directions from a static charge or magnetic pole. He argued that there had to be something special about the space around charged bodies since a current could be generated in an isolated coil of wire when it was spun in this type of space but not in ordinary space. Faraday believed that the lines of force were under tension like stretched elastic cords and that electrical energy resided in what he called "electrotonic" space to distinguish it from "empty" space.

Faraday was not a mathematician and his unmathematical explanations were not understood by the mathematicians. They seem to have drawn entirely wrong conclusions from his experimental evidence and his theory was given a very cool reception. To be understood and properly judged, the theory needed a mathematical interpreter, and that is what James Clerk Maxwell became.

Taking analogies from the theory of heat transfer and from the flow of fluid in pipes, he showed how Faraday's electrotonic state could be expressed in general mathematical terms. He also determined how the "lines of force" conception of an electric field led to the same mathematical result as the established "action at a distance" theory. In this way he eliminated an important argument that mathematicians had used to dismiss the theory.

In his fluid analogy, Maxwell compared electrical force to velocity of fluid and electrical potential to fluid pressure. Faraday's tubes of force were likened to the tubes for fluids and the surfaces of equal electric potential to the surfaces of equal pressure in a fluid. In this way Maxwell was able to account for electricity in motion (current electricity) as well as static electricity.

Maxwell published two papers on physical lines of force in 1861 and 1862. His greatest paper on electricity, "A Dynamical Theory of the Electromagnetic Field," appeared in 1864. It was a comprehensive mathematical treatment of the theory which showed the relationship between electric and magnetic forces and established the fact that electrical energy travels at a definite speed by means of electromagnetic waves. He applied the theory not only to electricity but to light, demonstrating that it is transmitted by the same mechanism. The experimental proof for the theory came only after Maxwell's death. In the 1880's a German physicist, Heinrich Hertz, detected electromagnetic waves transmitted over a distance and opened the way for modern radio transmission.

A unit of magnetic flux was eventually named for Maxwell. Since he had a ready sense of humor, he might have been amused had he known that science would use his name as one of its terms; he once had done the reverse—he had borrowed a scientific formula to replace his name. In the theory of thermodynamics there is an equation, $dp/dt = JCM$. Because his initials were J. C. M. he signed many of his letters and some of his published articles dp/dt.

12

WILLIAM THOMSON, LORD KELVIN 1824-1907

As a successor in these pages to James Clerk Maxwell no more appropriate personality could be found than William Thomson, better known in electrical history as Lord Kelvin. Both were Scots and outstanding in their mathematical attainments. They had in common an early aptitude for science and entered Scottish universities at an unusually early age, Thomson at Glasgow and Maxwell at Edinburgh. Both proceeded to Cambridge, England—Maxwell nine years after Thomson—where in turn they distinguished themselves by their academic attainments and took their places in the highest intellectual circles.

After Cambridge, however, their paths separated. In length of life and public recognition Thomson far outstripped his compatriot. He filled a crowded fifty years of scientific endeavor and the application of science as professor of natural philosophy in the University of Glasgow.

Thomson was a man of powerful imagination and, throughout his life, had a remarkable facility for combining the theoretical and the practical. Within hours of discussing, in the ablest possible way, the most abstruse phases of a scientific theory, he would turn his mind and hand to making a

COURTESY T. & R. ARMAN & SONS, LTD.

WILLIAM THOMSON, LORD KELVIN

new scientific instrument or solving some difficult engineering problem.

From his early days and throughout life he had the habit of placing quickly on record all important thoughts as soon as they came to him. These he followed up by a detailed analysis and a description of his experiments. Few men have left behind them such a wealth of original information as Thomson—over twenty printed books, between six and seven hundred scientific papers and lectures, and some seventy patents covering his various inventions.

William Thomson was born on June 26, 1824, in Belfast, Ireland. His father, James Thomson, who was then a professor of mathematics at the Royal Academical Institution of Belfast, had grown up on a farm in Ireland and worked his way through Glasgow University in Scotland. As a boy James Thomson developed an interest in the making of sundials. Once he also made a night dial with which he could tell time by one of the stars in the constellation Ursa Major. This he did without instruction, in the dim light of the cottage fire, using chalk and slate.

William Thomson's mother, who was the daughter of a Glasgow merchant, died when William was six, leaving her husband to bring up the boy, his eight-year-old brother, and his twelve-year-old sister.

About two years after his wife's death, Professor Thomson was offered a position at Glasgow University and moved from Ireland to Scotland with his family. In Belfast, he had taught his two boys at home, but at Glasgow, he took them with him to the university where they were allowed to sit in on classroom lectures. Before very long, both of them passed the university's entrance examinations, and William, at the age of ten, became a regular university student.

The story of the next few years reads like a romance, "the little tinkling bell in the top of the college tower calling college servants and workmen to work at six in the morning, the majestic great bell tolling at seven for the professors and finally the call bell to class rooms at seven thirty which students could only ignore at peril of being shut out by the janitor and missing the delights of a reading of Vergil or some other classical poet."

When William was fifteen a professor of astronomy called his attention to Fourier's *Analytical Theory of Heat,* the same book that had probably inspired Ohm when he formulated the laws governing the passage of electrical current along a wire. Although the book was in French and contained some difficult mathematics, William was ready to manage both, and so, as he later wrote, ". . . on 1st of May [1840], the very day the prizes were given, I took Fourier out of the University Library and in a fortnight I had mastered it—gone right through it."

William was very impressed by the book and became indignant when he learned that Fourier had been severely criticized in another book, *Theory of Heat,* by Philip Kelland (1808–1879). At the time when this happened the Thomson family was on the verge of setting out for a two months' vacation in Germany. Professor Thomson, who wanted his boys to learn German, had ruled that they should leave all their work behind, but William smuggled his copy of Fourier to Germany anyway. During a stay in Frankfurt he crept down into a cellar every day to study the conflict between Fourier's and Kelland's ideas. He decided that Kelland had not understood a basic conception of Fourier's and, to clear up the point, he wrote an article "On Fourier's Expansion of Functions in Trigonometrical Series." This paper, Thomson's first to be published, appeared somewhat later in the *Cambridge Mathematical Journal.*

When William finished his course at Glasgow after six years of study he was awarded a certificate showing that he had been approved for an A.B. degree. Still under sixteen, he did not apply for the degree because he and his father had decided that he should enter Cambridge University as an undergraduate and try to win top place in the Cambridge Mathematical Tripos. To score at the top of this examination was a very promising way to start an academic career, and this is what William had chosen to do with his future.

William Thomson started his Cambridge course in October 1841, and took up residence at St. Peter's College, better known by its ancient name, Peterhouse, and renowned in his time because of William Hopkins, a famous mathematical coach. Thomson had barely settled down to Cambridge life before the paper he had written and issued anonymously in Frankfurt appeared in the *Cambridge Mathematical Journal.* It aroused a great deal of interest among the mathematicians, and in spite of the pseudonym P. Q. R. which he had used, his identity soon became known. As a result, Thomson was singled out as a likely candidate to compete in the Tripos, and, in his second term, the great Hopkins became his private tutor.

To have Hopkins as a coach was the best thing any Cambridge mathematics student could hope for, and Thomson did not waste the opportunity. He began his day by meeting Hopkins at seven o'clock for reading appointments, and he worked long hours. Besides his routine studies he recorded ideas and theories in a well-ordered notebook and contributed several original papers to the *Cambridge Mathematical Journal.* In every way he outshone most of the other students, and the senior members of the university invited him to their family parties.

Although Thomson was a hard-working student, he was not a drudge. He enjoyed swimming, walking, and rowing and preferred rowing to walking because he thought it was better exercise for people without much time. In England, rowing is often a team sport, but Thomson favored what is known as "sculling" in a light, narrow, unstable boat called a "funny" that held only one or two people. When the famous Colquhoun rowing race was first held at Cambridge in November 1843 he was persuaded to enter and walked off with the silver sculls, the much-coveted prize.

In spite of his fondness for rowing Thomson hated to waste time, and he felt that sports should not interfere with studies. In one of his letters to his father he classified students as "rowing men" and "reading men." He chose friends from among the reading group and regarded the men who rowed in the college eight as "dissipated." Nevertheless, during his second year in college, he agreed to fill a vacancy in the boat for an annual race and found it "very exciting." Writing about the experience, he described how his team devised a plan to win by saving their strength at the beginning of the race so they could make a final push at the end. After putting this plan into effect his team won all their races, including the last one, in a wind and rain storm. He summed up his reaction to the races in this way: "During those three weeks of the races nothing occurring on the whole earth seemed of the slightest importance; we could talk and think of nothing else. It was three weeks clean cut out of my time for working at Cambridge; so I determined to do no more rowing."

Another of Thomson's extracurricular interests was music. At Cambridge he began to play a horn, the cornopean, and his diary tells about an incident when he and a friend were reminded that horns sounded very noisy after midnight. His musical ability was more appreciated when he played with a group at the first formal concert, presented in May 1844, given by the Cambridge Musical Society, which he and other Peterhouse musicians helped to found. All his life Thomson loved music and could identify the styles of different composers. His favorites were Beethoven, Mendelssohn, and particularly Weber.

Like many students, Thomson had trouble making his money stretch. "I have only half a crown left," he wrote home, and his father replied with a lecture about economizing but, as always, he sent money, too. In any case, finances were not the problem of William's college career that really worried either the father or the son, as both of them were determined that he should win the Mathematical Tripos. His rivals for the first place, that of the Senior Wrangler, were discussed in the long letters they wrote to each other. As the examination loomed nearer, William reported to his father that he ". . . had been going on reading steadily, about eight hours a day, and getting up regularly a little before six." "Do not relax," his father wrote back. "Do not relax, your persevering Johnian competitors may shoot ahead."

Although Thomson's coach, William Hopkins, was sure that his Peterhouse candidate's mathematical ability was unsurpassed in England, a coach at St. John's College regarded his candidate as unsurpassed in Europe. When the results of the Mathematical Tripos were announced, the St. John's candidate was named as Senior Wrangler and Thomson of Peterhouse was second. William wrote the sad news to Glasgow and received comforting replies. In a particularly reassuring letter, his sister Elizabeth wrote, "I was very sorry in reading your letter, when I came to the part where you say you are afraid Papa will think you have misspent your time at Cambridge. He does no such thing, he is very proud of his son, and not in the slightest degree less pleased with him since the small humiliation he has met with."

A few days after Thomson had heard the disappointing results of the Tripos, he was given good reason to feel better. He won the famous Smith's prize, which was considered the highest honor within the university although it was not as well known outside Cambridge as the Tripos. In this examination he came out ahead of the St. John's candidate, who won second place.

Thomson left Cambridge with a parting prize of twenty guineas from Peterhouse in his pocket. Armed with introductions to many scientists, he and a friend, Hugh Blackburn, set off for Paris, where they spent three months attending lectures at the Sorbonne and Collège de France and buying books not available in England. The cost of the journey from Cambridge to Paris was between five and six pounds, and the young men stayed in the university quarter where lodgings did not cost much. Although Thomson's father had told him to be careful of money he recognized his son's passion for unusual and sometimes expensive books on mathematics and sent him several extra five-pound notes. Following the usual custom of those times, he cut the notes in two and sent each half separately.

While in Paris, Thomson brought at least one important English scientific paper to the attention of French scientists. Among the lectures that he attended was a series by Henri Regnault, who is famous for his work on the theory of the steam engine. After one of the lectures, Thomson stayed to inspect Regnault's apparatus and wrote to his brother that he had seen ". . . a great many pretty things, of which they have a great abundance here, as the government gives them a great deal of money for apparatus for popular experiments and historical illustrations in the lectures." Soon after this incident, Thomson began to help out in Regnault's laboratory by working the air pump, stirring the water in the calorimeter, and performing other similar duties. By getting to the laboratory at eight each morning he was able to do some original work before the French experimenters arrived. With all his scientific interests, Thomson managed to visit the Paris Opera several times and also took lessons on the cornopean from a famous French music teacher.

When he returned to England, Thomson did some coaching at Cambridge and became a lecturer in mathematics there. Meanwhile, his father had been suggesting that there might be an opening for him at Glasgow where he himself, then nearly sixty, was still teaching. Even when William was still taking his final examinations at Cambridge his father had proposed his son as a candidate to succeed Professor Meikleham in the chair in natural philosophy, as the professor was ill and not expected to recover. Shortly after the professor's death, William applied for the post. He collected as many as thirty testimonials that praised him in such terms as "the first man of science of the rising generation in the country . . ." and as ". . . blessed with a reputation which veterans in science might envy." William's former tutor, William Hopkins, had this to say of him: "I doubt whether in the course of my long experience, I have ever met with any one of his own age who combines such a knowledge of abstract mathematics, with such an almost intuitive perception of physical truths, so accurate a knowledge of physical principles, and such enlarged and matured views of the great physical problems which Nature presents to us."

Along with his collection of references, Thomson sent twenty-six of his original papers to Glasgow. So impressed were the Glasgow faculty members that they passed over five more mature candidates and voted unanimously to give the chair to William, who was not yet twenty-two years old. On October 13, 1846, he went through the formalities of being appointed to the faculty. He presented a paper in Latin on a scientific subject that had been assigned to him a month before and took oaths to the Government, to the Church of Scotland, and to the university. The following month he began his teaching duties.

When William Thomson delivered his inaugural address at Glasgow he established a tradition which lasted for half a century. In a carefully prepared lecture on the scope and methods of physical science, he explained the relation of natural philosophy to other branches of human inquiry and laid a foundation for the theoretical and practical work of the class. He emphasized the fact that the science of force, that is, mechanics, kinetics, and statics, constituted the basis of natural philosophy, the subject in which he would specialize, and that every phenomenon in nature is a manifestation of force. Thus he placed dynamics at the head of physical science as a branch of applied mathematics. After ranging over the fields of pneumatics, acoustics, astronomy, and optics, he arrived at the specific divisions of natural philosophy which later became his greatest interests—heat, electricity, and magnetism. He expressed the intention of limiting the mathematical treatment "so that students qualified by the amount of mathematical preparation prescribed by the University regulations, before entering publicly on the Natural Philosophy course, may by careful attention and diligent private study, be able to follow his teaching." Drawing on the words of Bacon and of the psalmist he finally appealed for a reverence in the approach of the student to the wonders of the universe and his cooperation in the business of the class.

This remarkable lecture was repeated on the opening day of every session, and the well-worn manuscript which was used for over fifty years, with amendments made from time to time, is still in existence.

As a result of this earnest appeal and by means of his attractive personality, the young professor quickly made friends with the students, most of whom were about his own age. Among his more serious problems when he began teaching were the neglected, out-of-date classrooms and laboratory equipment. Fortunately he was able to persuade the university to agree to the necessary expenditures for improvement although the cost of a physics department was high compared with that of most other departments.

During the next few years Thomson spent his summer vacations traveling in Europe and visiting at Cambridge, where he served as a college examiner. When school was in session, he lived at the family home in Glasgow where his aunt kept house. These years were the last in his father's life, for old Professor Thomson died during the Glasgow cholera epidemic of 1848–49. Although William must have felt the loss keenly, he had many projects to divert his attention. At about this time he was lecturing on electromagnetism, experimenting with heat conduction, and submitting his first paper, "A Mathematical Theory of Magnetism," to the Royal Society, which elected him a Fellow in 1851.

At about this time Thomson also became interested in his cousin, Margaret Crum, a beautiful, well-educated girl whose father was a Fellow of the Royal Society and head of a famous calico printing firm. Thomson had known Margaret for a long time, and since his student days he had joined in family parties at Thornliebank near Glasgow, the home of the Crums. They were married on September 15, 1852, when William was twenty-eight and Margaret twenty-two.

After the couple's wedding trip to Wales, Thomson's output of scientific papers continued and, in quantity as well as quality, reached still higher peaks. In one remarkable piece of mathematical analysis, in which he studied the discharge of a Leyden jar, he laid the foundation of electrical oscillations which, through the later developments of Heinrich Hertz (1857–1894), became the basis of wireless telegraphy.

Meanwhile, a project was taking shape that was going to occupy a great deal of Thomson's time and thoughts and which was to make him a well-known public figure. In 1837 two Englishmen, Cooke and Wheatstone, had laid a commercial telegraph line along the railroad between London and Camden Town. A few years later, Morse transmitted signals between Boston, Massachusetts, and Washington, D.C. As telegraph systems developed, a demand arose for underwater cables. Although the problem of finding an insulating material, or dielectric, presented a temporary obstacle, it was solved by the discovery of a new gum, gutta-percha. In 1851 a cable was laid across the English Channel which operated successfully between England and France for many years.

The success of this cable proved that submarine telegraphy was a sound engineering proposition. Other underwater lines were laid in various parts of the world, with England's new cable-making industry supplying many of the materials. As the system of cables spread, people began to discuss the possibility of a telegraphic link between Europe and America.

At first the idea of a direct cable across the Atlantic was dismissed as impractical. The Western Union Company, which had already built an extensive network of land lines over the United States, proposed an indirect route across Asia that would require a smaller reach of underwater cable. They planned to carry a line up along the western coast of Canada and then westward across the southern coast of Alaska and the long chain of the Aleutian Islands to the Bering Sea and Siberia. The construction of this cable was begun and a considerable part of it had been set up when the project was dropped in favor of a direct Atlantic cable.

The transatlantic cable project was one of the biggest and most risky ventures of its time because of the weight and cost of the cable that would have to be used underwater and the unknown hazards of the ocean bed. To finance the manufacture and laying of the cable, a New York financier named Cyrus Field organized the Atlantic Telegraph Company with a capital of £350,000 on October 20, 1856. A few weeks later, Professor William Thomson joined the company as one of its directors. His presence in the company boosted its prestige, for, quite correctly, people judged that his scientific knowledge would give the project a far greater chance of success.

When Thomson joined the company, the form of the cable had already been decided. There was to be a strand of seven conducting wires in it in case any of them broke. As insulation, three separate coats of gutta-percha were to be applied to the cable in case any of the layers should have leaks. The over-all armoring of the two-thousand-mile length of line was to be strengthened over the shore end, which was often rocky. In contrast to this careful planning to prevent mistakes, there was a race against time in manufacturing the cable, which used more than 20,000 miles of copper wire, more than 380,000 miles of iron wire, and 300 tons of gutta-percha. The haste of manufacturing probably added to the troubles that beset the subsequent cable-laying expedition.

By the summer of 1857 the cable was ready; half of it was carried by the British ship *Agamemnon,* and half by the United States ship *Niagara.* At mid-Atlantic the two ships were to meet, splice the ends, and separate to pay out the cable east to Europe and west to America.

When the British ship was setting out on the cable-laying expedition a Mr. Whitehead, who was to be the electrician for the project, said that he could not make the voyage because of ill-health. The real reason may have been something else, for he had had several technical disagreements with Professor Thomson and seemed to resent him. In any case, Thomson agreed to take Whitehead's place. It was a fortunate change in plans since Thomson's experiences on the voyage inspired him to make several inventions and confirmed some of his theories on the transmission of telegraph signals.

From the start, the expedition ran into trouble. Finally the ships returned to port and the cable laying was postponed until the following year. Thomson returned to his teaching duties, but he did not put the cable project completely out of his mind. For one thing, he was interested in developing a more sensitive galvanometer to receive weak signals since he was convinced that the voltage needed to operate the existing insensitive instruments would add to the risk of a cable breakdown.

He replaced the suspended magnet in the galvanometer with a tiny piece of magnetized watch spring cemented to the back of a silvered glass mirror. The arrangement was suspended by a single fiber of natural silk. A lamp was placed so that a beam of light was reflected from the mirror and cast a spot of light on a scaled surface placed some distance away. As the mirror turned in response to signals, the spot of light moved on the scale. Even a slight movement of the mirror produced a very noticeable change in the position of the spot of light on the scale because of its distance from the mirror. The mirror galvanometer, which could pick up very faint signals, became very important in submarine telegraphy and many other branches of electrical science.

This was not the only improvement that Thomson developed for telegraphy in the winter of 1857–58. He studied the mechanics of cable laying in deep water and invented an improved cable brake to regulate the way the cable line was paid out as it descended to the ocean floor.

Thomson was also concerned about the material in the cable. When he went back to Glasgow after the expedition failed, he took along some pieces of the still unlaid line because he suspected that there were differences in the conductivity of the copper used. The tests he made on the samples confirmed his suspicion, and he wrote a paper for the British Association that helped to improve the future quality of submarine cables. Although he had difficulty in persuading his co-directors in the Atlantic Telegraph Company that it was important to specify high-conductivity copper for the cable he proceeded to set up one of the first industrial-testing laboratories to control the quality of copper used by the company.

During the summer of 1858 the two cable-laying ships set sail once more with Professor Thomson in the expedition. Again bad luck dogged the enterprise. Even before the mid-Atlantic splice could be made, severe storms damaged the ships, splitting their deck planks and flooding the instrument rooms. Again the ships had to return to port and make a fresh start. During this setback, Thomson continued to test his equipment, and his refusal to admit the possibility of failure helped to keep up the spirits of the rest of the expedition. The ships sailed out for a second time that summer, and, finally, the two ends of the cable were landed in Europe and America. On August 17, 1858, the first message was transmitted across the Atlantic. The event was celebrated on both sides of the ocean, and the British queen and American president exchanged congratulations. The cable worked, but not for long: within a few weeks its signals grew weaker, and after transmitting some seven hundred messages, it failed completely.

Meanwhile, other cables that had been operating successfully for several years started to break down. Since the failures caused a great financial loss for British firms, the British government called for a public inquiry to consider the problems of telegraphy. At the hearing, which lasted from December 1, 1859, to September 4, 1860, Professor Thomson was one of the major witnesses.

One of the most important subjects taken up at the inquiry was the speed at which a signal traveled through a long insulated conductor. Thomson had a great deal to say on this question. From his Cambridge days he had been greatly influenced by the work of Fourier on heat transmission. He now applied the same mathematical treatment to the transmission of electricity along an insulated conductor such as a submarine cable. For the first time he showed that the retardation in the transmission of a signal—which, incidentally, had already been observed on some of the earlier European cables—was directly proportional to the capacity (K) and to the resistance (R) and so formulated the famous KR law. He drew two conclusions of great practical importance. As both K and R were proportioned to the length of the cable, the retardation was proportional to the *square* of the length—doubling the length increased the retardation four times. Or, if a cable 200 miles long had a retardation of one tenth of a second, a length 2,000 miles of the same cable would have a retardation one hundred times as great, or ten seconds.

He thus clarified a vital economic point in the use of long submarine cables. The retardation could be reduced, and thus the speed of working increased by reducing the capacity—that is, by increasing the thickness of the insulation—

and reducing the resistance by using a heavier conductor.

After the publication of the government report, and much further discussion of the various factors now known to affect the reliability of submarine cables, along with additional experience in the Persian Gulf, public confidence was restored and in 1864 Mr. Field succeeded in raising £600,000 for a still further attempt to bridge the Atlantic. Thomson was elected to a scientific committee to select the design of cable to be used, and this time a cable with 300 pounds of copper and 400 pounds of gutta-percha per mile was adopted.

The only ship available for carrying the cable in one length was Brunel's *Great Eastern,* which was lying idle, having failed commercially. When she sailed on July 14, 1865, Thomson was on board. Two mechanical faults had been traced and repaired and twelve hundred miles had been laid when the cable parted in midocean. Although on August 16 the *Great Eastern* reappeared at Valentia harbor in Ireland, this time there was no depression. All those concerned were confident that the cause of the failure would be avoided in future, while Thomson publicly declared his conviction that the lost end could be recovered even though it lay at a depth of two miles.

The extent to which he had risen in public esteem at the age of forty-one is shown by an incident which occurred at this time. His preparations for the new expedition took him on frequent trips between Glasgow and London in connection with the manufacture of his instruments by the celebrated firm of Whites. One day his secretary took a message to the Glasgow railroad depot a few minutes before the train for London was due to leave—"I have gone to Whites to hurry on an instrument. The London mail train must on no account start tonight until I come." The train waited.

The following year the *Great Eastern*, once more with the Glasgow professor on board, sailed west, this time with a complete new length of cable and the previously unlaid portion. Everything went according to plan and on September 8 there were two complete cables across the Atlantic. Traffic followed quickly but not before the sensitivity of Thomson's instrument at Valentia had been demonstrated by a dramatic test. A clear message was received from Newfoundland using the current from a battery made up of a gun cap containing one drop of acidulated water and a tiny strip of zinc. On his return to England Queen Victoria conferred on Thomson the honor of knighthood in recognition of his great achievements.

During his association with submarine telegraphy Thomson had conceived the idea of adapting his mirror galvanometer in such a way as to print a permanent record of received signals and, after many trials of different devices, he produced the siphon recorder, an instrument of outstanding ingenuity and usefulness. A light coil was delicately suspended between the poles of a powerful magnet so that a small current flowing through the coil caused it to turn to the right or to the left, depending on the direction of the current. Attached to the suspended coil was a very fine glass tube bent to form a siphon and filled with ink. By means of an electric charge the ink was made to flow from the open end of the tube which faced, but did not quite touch, a moving strip of paper. In this way any series of signals received by the coil was recorded as a wavy line on the moving ribbon. The first perfected instrument, which was exhibited in

1870, raised the speed of reception from 35 words per minute to 120.

During the summer of 1869 Thomson became very concerned at the state of his wife's health, which deteriorated in the fall to such an extent that they were forced to cancel a winter trip to the south. The doctor gave no hope of recovery, but Mrs. Thomson lived on until the following summer, dying on June 17, 1870. Her loss was a severe blow to Thomson; there was no family.

With the conclusion of the Atlantic cable project he turned his attention once again to abstract studies, atomic physics, the rigidity and age of the earth, and many others. He also became interested in the improvement of the mariner's compass and designed one which avoided the many defects of existing types. In the same field of navigation he invented a deep-sea-sounding apparatus and a tide-predicting machine. He also served on an admiralty committee investigating the scientific design of ships.

William Thomson was always fond of the sea and with the income he was now receiving from his many electrical inventions he purchased a 126-ton sailing yacht, the *Lalla Rookh,* and for many years spent most of his university vacations on the yacht with various parties of friends, sailing from the Hebrides to the Canaries and in the Mediterranean.

In June 1873—three years after the death of his wife Margaret—Thomson met Frances Anna Blandy in Madeira and a friendship grew up between them which a year later led to marriage. The second Lady Thomson was a good sailor, and they spent many happy days on the *Lalla Rookh.* After his second marriage Thomson bought a piece of ground at Largs and built a mansion, Netherhall, whose name remains closely associated with Kelvin, the name that Thomson later assumed for his peerage. Lady Thomson was welcomed into the family and conducted his household with grace and distinction for the next thirty years.

Among the vast range of activities he continued to pursue in addition to his university duties was his work on the Electrical Standards Committee, which had been set up in 1861 by the British Association. He was able to persuade the other committee members to adopt absolute units on the Weber system, which has already been discussed in an earlier chapter. He also devised an important modification of Weber's rotating-coil apparatus for determining the absolute unit of resistance. He had the apparatus made in Glasgow by his associate James White, the instrument maker, and then cooperated with Maxwell and others when the classical experiments were carried out at King's College, London. He also continued his voluminous correspondence, among which his letters to the German physicist Hermann Helmholtz are outstanding, and took a prominent part in international electrical conferences. In one of these, held in Paris, the names of the electrical units ohm, volt, farad, and coulomb were agreed to and, at his suggestion, the ampere—without the accent—was adopted for the unit of current.

As the years passed, celebrations of various kinds took much of Thomson's time and attention. His jubilee at Glasgow University in 1896 was a most impressive three-day function; delegates from many universities and other distinguished visitors numbered twenty-five hundred. A large exhibition of instruments which he had invented created great interest.

Although he was now approaching the end of his life he

continued to lecture and write. In February 1907 he declined a proposed third term as president of the Institution of Electrical Engineers, explaining, in a letter, that "it is impossible for me to accept the honour without neglecting arrears of work which I have promised from time to time during the last fifty years"—but he succumbed to persuasion. As things turned out, he was not well enough to attend the inaugural meeting, and three days later he peacefully passed away.

Today a slab in the stone floor of Westminster Abbey near the tomb of the great Newton bears the simple inscription

WILLIAM THOMSON
LORD KELVIN
1824–1907

BIBLIOGRAPHY

FRANKLIN

Bernard K. Cohen, *Benjamin Franklin's Experiments*. Cambridge, Mass.: Harvard University Press, 1941

GALVANI

Luigi Galvani, *Effects of Electricity on Muscular Motion* (1791). Facsimile of original Latin edition with English translation by Margaret Glover Foley. Norwalk, Conn.: Burndy Library, 1953.

VOLTA

Sac Gallisto Grandi, *Alessandro Volta* (in Italian). Milan, 1899.

DAVY

Anne Treneer, *The Mercurial Chemist, A Life of Sir Humphry Davy*. London: Methuen, 1963.

John Davy, *The Life of Sir Humphry Davy*. London, 1831.

OERSTED

Bern Dibner, *Oersted and the Discovery of Electromagnetism*. Norwalk, Conn.: Burndy Library, 1961.

AMPÈRE

Louis de Launay, *Le Grand Ampère* (in French). Librairie Académique Perrin, 1925.

FARADAY

Bence Jones, *Life and Letters of Faraday*. Longmans Green & Company, 1870.

HENRY

Thomas Coulson, *Joseph Henry—His Life and Work.* Princeton, N.J.: Princeton University Press, 1950.

Joseph Henry, Scientific Writing (2 vols.) Smithsonian Institution, 1886.

OHM

W. Francis, ed., *The Galvanic Circuit Investigated Mathematically* (Vol. II of *Taylor's Scientific Memoirs*). Translated from the German, 1827. New York, 1891.

GAUSS

Sartorius von Waltershausen, *Gauss, zum Gedächtniss* (in German), 2nd ed. 1877.

WEBER

Heinrich Weber, *Wilhelm Weber, Eine Lebenskizze* (in German) Breslau: Verlag von Eduard Trewendt, 1893.

MAXWELL

Campbell and Garnett, *Life of James Clerk Maxwell.* Macmillan, 1882.

KELVIN

Silvanus P. Thompson, *Life of Lord Kelvin.* Macmillan, 1910.

INDEX

Index

ABOUT THE AUTHOR

One of England's eminent electrical engineers, Dr. Percy Dunsheath, C.B.E., is also well known to young people through his lectures on electricity and its early beginnings held at the Royal Institution in London and elsewhere. Dr. Dunsheath has spent many years as director of research in the British cable industry and, during the Second World War, made major contributions in the destruction of magnetic mines and the underwater transmission of gasoline from England to France.

He is a past chairman of the Cambridge Instrument Company, Ltd., and a past president of the Institution of Electrical Engineers, the British Electrical Development Association, and the International Electrotechnical Commission.

Dr. Dunsheath was born in Sheffield, England, and holds degrees from the University of Sheffield, Cambridge University, and London University and is still a Senator at the latter. Several of his numerous books and articles on electricity have been published in this country.

A frequent traveler on the Continent, Dr. Dunsheath has also paid many visits to the United States, Canada, India, Kashmir, New Zealand, and Australia. Water-color painting is one of his major hobbies, and his pictures have appeared in many exhibitions.

Dr. Dunsheath and his wife, the well-known British mountaineer, live in Surrey, England.